This Vital Air
This Vital Water

Man's

Environmental Crisis

This Vital Air This Vital Water

Man's Environmental Crisis

By THOMAS G. AYLESWORTH

Illustrated with photographs

Rand McNally & Company

Chicago   New York   San Francisco

TO VIRGINIA,

MY WIFE

Contents

Acknowledgments

The author is deeply indebted to the Bureau of Disease Prevention and Control, United States Public Health Service, and the Federal Water Pollution Control Administration, United States Department of the Interior, for their help in the preparation of this book; also to Dr. I. Robert Ehrlich, whose corrections and suggestions were so valuable; and to Mrs. Lillian McClintock, a book editor whose patience and energy are inexhaustible.

The photographs on pages 63 and 78 are from the National Center for Air Pollution Control (the latter appeared originally in the Muskegon (Mich.) *Chronicle*); all other photographs are from the Federal Water Pollution Control Administration, United States Department of the Interior, although some of them originated elsewhere, as follows: page 12 in *London* (England) *Daily Mirror* (Mirrorpic); page 13 in *Topical Press,* London, England; page 15 in New York *Daily News;* pages 25, 51 (top), 76, 83 (bottom), 164, 174, and 176 (center and bottom) from United States Public Health Service; page 31 from New York Botanical Gardens; page 34 in Los Angeles *Times;* page 51 from Los Angeles County Air Pollution Control District; page 61 in *Chicago Tribune;* page 83 (top) in St. Louis *Post-Dispatch;* page 83 (center) in *San Francisco News-Call Bulletin;* page 113 (bottom) in Cleveland *Plain Dealer;* page 150 in St. Louis *Post-Dispatch* (Art Witman, photographer); page 157 from National Aeronautics and Space Administration; and page 176 (top) from Wayne State University, Detroit, Michigan.

The author is grateful for permission to use these pictures.

Illustrations

1

The Deadly Sky

It began on December 1, 1930. A fine mist covered almost all of Belgium. In the Meuse Valley, with its iron and steel works, zinc smelters, and gas plants, the mist was particularly heavy. The fog combined with the smoke from the coal fires used in these industrial plants and gradually became thicker and thicker until, on December 3, illnesses began to occur.

Shortness of breath was the first complaint. But soon it seemed as if the whole population were coughing. In all, several thousand cases of respiratory disease were reported. During the four days that the smog—a combination of smoke and fog—lasted, sixty-three deaths, traceable to air pollution, were recorded. Most of the illnesses and deaths occurred among the elderly, but even young children were affected.

Donora, Pennsylvania, is a small town on the Monongahela River about thirty miles south of Pittsburgh. It is the center of a vast industrial complex. There are steel mills, a wire plant, zinc smelters, and coke plants nearby. Not only that, but Donora lies in a pocket with hills both to the east and to the west. The townspeople were used to dirty air, but on the murky morning of October 26, 1948, many of them must have thought that the sun had not come up.

By October 28, the residents of Donora knew that they had never seen anything as bad as this before. A heavy smog had settled over the city and was to stay until October 31. Industrial waste kept pouring into the atmosphere. Zinc fumes, coal smoke, and fly ash shut out the sun. Soot fell out of the gloom and was so thick that footprints could be seen on the sidewalk. The sickening air seemed to have the taste of sulfur dioxide.

The physicians' offices were swamped. One doctor said, "I didn't have time to think or wonder. . . . It was about impossible to drive. I even had trouble finding the office. I got out of the car and my chest felt tight. . . . I started coughing and I couldn't stop. I didn't have the strength to answer the phone."

Shortness of breath and coughing were not the only complaints. People developed sore throats, headaches, eye irritations, and nausea. On October 29, seventeen people died as a result of the pollution. By October 31, when a heavy rain fell and washed away the smog, twenty people had perished and almost six thousand of Donora's fourteen thousand residents had become ill.

A little more than two years later, in 1950, tragedy struck again. This time the place was Poza Rica, Mexico, a town of about fifteen thousand people, situated on the

Gulf of Mexico east of Mexico City. It is surrounded by natural-gas fields. One of the by-products of the fields is hydrogen sulfide, from which a local industry produces sulfur.

At about five o'clock on the morning of November 24, there was an accident at the factory. Huge amounts of hydrogen sulfide were released into the air, and, unfortunately, it was a hazy, foggy morning. Although the episode lasted less than an hour, twenty-two people were killed and three hundred twenty were hospitalized.

The worst air pollution tragedy in history occurred in London two years later. December 3, 1952, was one of the most delightful days of the winter. A cold front had passed through during the night, and a pleasant wind was blowing in from the north. By noon the temperature was higher than 40 degrees and the relative humidity was just about 70 percent. The clear sky was filled with cumulus clouds.

But the next day the wind changed, the temperature began to drop, the humidity to rise, and dark gray stratus clouds began to move over the area. The smell of smoke was in the air—smoke from thousands of coal fires in homes and factories, along with fly ash and such noxious gases as sulfur dioxide.

By December 6, a dense fog blotted out the sky and visibility was measured in tens of feet. Airplanes were not flying and automobiles were at a standstill. Humidity was up to 100 percent, temperature was below freezing, and the air was deadly calm. London bobbies, who had to be outside, wore surgical masks to protect their lungs.

One of the British newspapers commented that the sun "hung sulkily in the dirty sky with no more radiance than an unlit Chinese lantern."

Still the stoves, furnaces, and fireplaces belched their poisons into the air. The airborne garbage attacked all living things. Eyes watered, throats burned, hospitals filled up, and the death toll began to rise. On December 10, a cold front passed over London, and people could breathe again. What had been the toll? During the smog, four thousand people died as a direct result of pollution, and during the next two months eight thousand more died after lingering illnesses because of this tragedy.

These examples are only the worst. Countless other

The London killer smog in Piccadilly Circus hung over the streets and prevented any flow of traffic

During the London disaster of 1956, bus company employees sometimes carried burning torches to lead the driver through the smog

episodes have been recorded. In 1956, London had another disaster that killed one thousand people, and in 1962, four hundred more died from air pollution. In 1953, over two hundred New Yorkers died as a direct result of smog. Again, in New York, in 1963, two hundred more people died; and in 1966, one hundred sixty-eight died after a Thanksgiving weekend of intense air pollution.

New Yorkers had been warned. For several months, when they turned on their television sets, they saw commercials prepared by the Citizens for Clean Air, Inc. The same organization ran newspaper advertisements. "Tomorrow morning when you get up, take a nice deep breath," one of the ads said. "It'll make you feel rotten."

Then came the long Thanksgiving weekend of 1966, and with it, a dirty, yellow smog. The air pollution index, based on measurements of the amounts of sulfur dioxide, carbon dioxide, and smoke in the air, shot up to 60. And the emergency level is 50. Immediately, the city health department warned citizens with heart, lung, and upper respiratory ailments to stay indoors. This they were glad to do, because outside it hurt them to breathe.

The part of the air pollution index reading based on the sulfur dioxide measurements stood at close to one part per million parts of air. The normal reading is about two-tenths of a part per million. Other measurements began pouring in. Carbon monoxide hit 10 ppm, and dust particles were at 7.5 ppm. An alert was called, and health authorities began to count their blessings. It was a good thing it was a holiday, when few industrial furnaces were operating and when people did not have to work, making emergency warning directions easier to obey.

All residents of the city and all building superintendents were asked to reduce indoor temperatures to 60 degrees. This helped cut down on the smoke from heating plants. The garbage incinerators all over the city were shut down. People were asked not to drive unless it was absolutely necessary. There was almost complete cooperation, but in the meantime, almost two thousand tons of refuse piled up. Naturally, the incinerators had to start up again. However, soon after this the weather changed and the smog left the city.

New York City does have some clear days . . . until the smog rolls in

Few people were made ill by the smog, but this was probably because of the excellent cooperation given the health department and the fact that the haze lasted only a few days. As it was, an estimated 10 percent of the people in New York City suffered from smarting eyes, breathing difficulties, coughing, and wheezing. If this smog had been as bad as the Donora disaster, eleven thousand people would have died and four million would have become ill.

At the time, H. H. Slater, a federal meteorologist, issued a warning. He said New York City was so polluted that if an equal amount of pollution existed in the air of most other cities, the atmosphere would be unfit for human consumption. But he added that New York was fortunate to have a healthy wind, fewer inversions, and more cleansing rain than most cities enjoy.

What caused these tragedies in London and New York? After all, people are rather used to living in a polluted atmosphere. Dirt, dust, gases, and soot are always with us. How do they build up from time to time so that suddenly man cannot live in his poisonous air?

First of all, there were vast amounts of smoke pouring out of homes and factories during these emergencies. Secondly, weather conditions were such that a situation called a thermal inversion was present.

We know that as you go up in an airplane, the temperature of the outside air usually drops. Generally, the higher you go, the colder it is. We also know that warm air tends to rise. So, as the warm air rises, it cools off as it expands, due to lower pressure, and mixes with the cooler air above. And as the warm air rises, it carries away a great deal of the pollution from the ground level.

But there are times, in the movement of air and weather, when a mass of warm air will move into a region occupied by cold air. The warm air, being lighter, will rise above the colder, heavier mass of air, resulting in a situation that is the reverse of the usual one. This condition, called an "inversion," is extremely stable and may last for many days. Now, when pollution-laden warm air rises through the colder air near the ground and meets the warmer air, it is no longer lighter than its surroundings. It is trapped between the two layers and, as it cools, will find its way back to the ground with its aerial garbage.

Now add another condition. Where there is an inversion, generally there is little wind to carry away the smog. (In Donora and in London there was no wind at all.) Therefore, since the air cannot move aloft to carry away the pollutants, and there is no wind to blow them away, the contamination concentration builds and builds until the weather changes. If it continues to build long enough, there will be danger ahead.

But these tragedies are only the kinds of pollution stories that make the headlines of your newspapers. They occur seldom, but can happen in any city. In the United States, in addition to New York, very serious situations have occurred in Los Angeles, Washington, D.C., and Philadelphia, to name just a few places.

Terrible as these fatal fogs are, they are isolated end results of excess contamination. The fight against air pollution must begin long before these horrible events happen. The fight must begin before many people are aware that a problem exists.

2

The Constant Problem

Air pollution has probably been with us since our ancient ancestors discovered fire. But in those long-ago days, the smoke, unburned carbon particles, soot, and gases rose in the air and were carried away by the wind. Air pollution did not begin to be a problem until men began living in towns and cities and started to burn many fires close to each other at the same time.

For thousands of years, though, in the Middle East, the farmers have burned brush and grass. These large fires have caused much local pollution.

And almost seven hundred years ago—in 1273—King Edward I of England passed the first law that included an attempt to control smoke. Rules were laid down restricting the use of fire. Shortly after this, in 1306, the English government passed another pollution law. This forbade any person to burn coal while Parliament was in session. It is said that one man was hanged for disobeying this law.

Until the sixteenth century, people who were lucky enough to own silver did not have to polish it. It never tarnished. But as the uses of coal and fuel oil began to increase, black deposits caused by sulfur gases began to form on silver plates, pots, and other utensils.

The first book ever written about air pollution came along in 1661. This book, written by the British reporter John Evelyn, contained the first list of scientific solutions to the air pollution problem. Its title, which may sound a bit odd to us today, was *FUMIFUGIUM: OR The Inconvenience of the AER, AND SMOAKE of LONDON DISSIPATED Together With some Remedies Humbly Proposed by J. E. Esq.; To His Sacred Majestie, and to the Parliament Assembled. Published by His Majesties Command.*

Evelyn described in detail the smog over London. But more than this, he warned that the cause of the haze was the burning of so much coal in the manufacturing plants which were springing up all over the city. Truly, he was man's first pollution-control expert.

In Evelyn's time, the people of the American colonies were having relatively little trouble with their air. They enjoyed fine breezes that carried away the smoke from their fires. After all, they lived in small towns or on farms surrounded by huge open spaces. At that time, even New York City had only about one thousand residents. But about two hundred years later, in 1873, magazine articles began to appear in the United States warning about the "organic dust" that was polluting the air of the cities. And at that time the country's population was about one-fifth of what it is today.

Today, the air pollution problem is to be found all

over the world. Tokyo had sixty-four serious smog warn-
ings in 1966 alone. This city now has as much as four
times more cases of bronchitis per thousand residents
than are found in the rest of Japan. Traffic policemen in
Tokyo, during the rush hour, stop directing traffic every
half hour to breathe pure oxygen from tanks placed at
street intersections. Pollution is a problem in other parts
of the country, too. Schoolchildren in Yokkaichi, when
they play, sometimes have to wear surgical masks that
have been treated with chemicals to protect them from
industrial pollution. American troops stationed in parts
of Japan (as well as in Okinawa) have developed the
"Tokyo-Yokohama disease." This illness produces a
cough, indigestion, and shortness of breath. It is connected with air pollution, and the effects, in some cases,
are permanent.

In Greece, near Athens, every Monday morning,
when the factories start production after the weekend,
the smog begins to build up. It spreads over the low-
lying sections of town and eventually reaches the Acrop-
olis and the Parthenon. For over two thousand years,
parts of the Parthenon were almost unchanged. We
know this because plaster casts of some of the statues
were made in 1802. In 1965 those plaster casts were com-
pared with the statues as they are now. Some of the old
treasures are almost unrecognizable because of the cor-
rosive effects of air pollution.

The Ruhr Valley of West Germany is a region of
heavy industry. Warning signs can now be seen telling
motorists that in case of excessive air pollution, they must

get off the road. In this region, the soot is so bad that, for white-collar workers, three clean shirts a day seems to be the rule rather than the exception. Elsewhere in West Germany, stone arches and girders are having to be replaced at a fantastic rate. The Cologne Cathedral has a large permanent team of stonemasons and architects just to repair the damage caused by air pollution.

East Germany has not escaped the blight, either. The citizens there have been so moved by a novel called *The Divided Sky*, by Christa Wolf, telling of the dangers of both air and water pollution, that steps are being taken to prevent pollution damage. Now there is a program going on to develop systems to trap sulfur dioxide coming from the chemical industries' smokestacks; power plants are being required to trap fly ash and soot; and research is being conducted to find better sewage-treatment techniques.

In France, a law has been passed that requires automobile exhaust to be recycled through the engine to complete the incomplete burning of gasoline. In the French Alps the evergreen trees are being killed by fluoride that is given off by metal plants. A group of statues— "La Danse," by Carpeaux, on the front of the Opéra in Paris—has had to be replaced.

Padua, Italy, is losing some of its art treasures, too. Some frescoed walls painted by Giotto in the fourteenth century are crumbling. Air pollution in Florence is destroying the Ponte Vecchio, the Pitti Palace, and the Basilica of San Lorenzo.

Spain is suffering also. Madrid coughs its way

through clouds of nitrogen and sulfur fumes almost every morning—sometimes until noon. The air pollution content of the city went up almost 20 percent in two years. The cause, probably, is that there are more diesel engines, more coal burning, and more outdoor bonfires. One Madrid citizen recently said, "When I take my first deep breath of air in the morning, I fill my lungs with enough gas to make my car run all day."

In South America, the cities of São Paulo in Brazil, and Santiago in Chile, are in the midst of a pollution problem. São Paulo has doubled its population since World War II and now has about five million people. Because of the fifty thousand new industrial plants and factories in the city, ten tons of hydrofluoric acid and one thousand tons of sulfuric anhydride are dumped into the air each day. São Paulo has had a 100 percent increase in deaths due to bronchial diseases, while the neighboring city of Rio de Janeiro—a city with a much lower rate of industrial growth—has cut its bronchial deaths in half. In Santiago, thirty tons of dust per square mile fall on the city every month.

3

Solids in the Air

Air pollutants can be broken down into seven general categories for the sake of discussion: fine particles, sulfur dioxide, carbon monoxide, smog reactants, total oxidants, radioactive pollutants, and miscellaneous pollutants. The most obvious type of pollutant is the fine particle, since trillions of these particles come rolling out in the smoke from the world's millions of chimneys.

These chimneys are in homes, in factories and power plants, in incinerators, and in garbage dumps. Everywhere we look, we seem to see smoke. And in the smoke will be found fine particles of such substances as carbon and soot, fly ash, oil, grease, and even metals of various types. If these fine particles are heavy enough, they will fall to earth and begin their work of soiling furniture, clothing, and faces. If they do not fall, they will remain in the air until they are blown away, in the meantime reducing visibility or entering our lungs.

But chimney smoke is not the only source of fine particles. Some industries, in their grinding and drying operations, and even housewives shaking out dustcloths, contribute particles to the atmosphere. A single strong eruption of a volcano can throw one hundred billion cubic yards of particles into the air. Tiny drops of sea-water rise from the ocean, dry in the air, and leave behind microscopic particles of salt.

We even get particles from outer space. One thousand tons of micrometeorites fall on the earth each year. Growing plants give off gases that may condense to form tiny liquid particles in the air. If you have ever seen a haze forming over a forest of trees, you have seen the result of this.

While we usually think that the automobile pollutes the air only with exhaust gases, it also contributes fine particles to the atmosphere—equal to eight-tenths of one percent of the original weight of the gasoline burned in the engine. Half of these particles are tiny bits of lead from the tetraethyl lead used in the gasoline to prevent engine knock. Chlorine, bromine, and carbon particles also come out of automobiles. The chlorine and bromine are added to gasoline, as was the tetraethyl lead, to improve engine performance; the carbon is one of the products of the combustion.

Automobiles contribute still another particle to the atmosphere—rubber. We know that rolling, slipping, spinning, and sliding tires wear down. As they wear, they throw off particles. In one survey it was estimated that fifty tons of rubber particles fall every day on the streets of Los Angeles.

In 1959 it was found that over ten thousand tons of solid matter were being discharged daily into the air by industry in the Chicago area alone. An average of forty-three tons of pollution dustfall per square mile per month falls on Chicago. The island of Manhattan, containing only about 7 percent of the total area of New York City, has an annual particle fallout of twenty thousand tons.

Of course we are all familiar with the immediate effects of fine particles in the air. They make things dirty —automobiles, buildings, clothing, windows, and people. But some of their other effects are much more subtle. Carbon particles have a well-known ability to adsorb gases, that is, to attract large quantities of certain gases on their surfaces. It is this property that makes carbon so popular in the manufacture of gas masks—it is able to adsorb most common poisonous gases, thereby removing

Fine particle fallout is a nuisance

them from the air passing through the mask. When these same carbon particles in the atmosphere are breathed into our lungs, they may also have many poisonous gases from the atmosphere adsorbed on their surface. This adsorption may permit a quicker penetration into the lungs by the dangerous chemical than would ordinarily be possible.

Some more exotic effects on humans are caused by fine particles, but they seem most often to be directly connected with specific allergies. However, some medical researchers feel that there may be a connection between a rise in the soot content of the air and an increase in the number of cases of pneumonia.

One very serious connection between particles in the air and human health is pointed out by a geochemist at the California Institute of Technology. Dr. Clair C. Patterson has found that lead particles in the air may affect our central nervous systems. Another particle in the air—cadmium—may have a connection with heart disease. Dr. Robert E. Carroll of the United States Public Health Service has noticed that cities with high concentrations of cadmium in the air have higher than normal death rates from heart disease. Some of these cities are Chicago, New York, Newark, Philadelphia, and Indianapolis. On the other hand, cities such as Las Vegas, Eugene, and Chattanooga, with low cadmium concentrations, have lower than normal death rates from heart disease. Dr. Carroll also says that this cadmium in the air probably comes from ore-smelting plants.

Dr. Vincent Schaefer, of the Atmospheric Sciences Research Center of the State University of New York, blames lead in the air for some extra rain. Particles of this material can, under proper conditions, act in the same way as the silver iodide crystals often used for cloud seeding. The lead combines with iodine high in the air. Then, if there is very cold water vapor present, ice crystals form in the clouds. The ice crystals serve as the nucleus, or central core, of the raindrop.

Soot can be a financial problem. Although stories of costs incurred because of grime can fill volumes, one of the most startling is the story of the dirt on the front of the New York Hilton Hotel. Because of fly ash and soot on the front of the building, it was so badly discolored that a fifty-thousand-dollar cleaning job was necessary. How long did it take to get so dirty? Three and one-half years!

Even the astronomers, who should be concentrating on things in outer space instead of in our own atmosphere, are up in arms. Dr. Orren Mohler of the University of Michigan states the case: "Haze layers in the atmosphere are bad. When they reflect artificial lights they raise the luminosity of the entire sky to the level of the faintest stars, making it impossible to observe them."

Though there are many kinds of fine particles in our air, and they are the most obvious pollutants, they are not the most common. Actually, it is estimated that these particles are responsible for only 10 percent of the pollution in the air over the United States.

4

Gases in the Air

One of the most dangerous gaseous pollutants is sulfur dioxide. At least it seems to be the most dangerous to man. It attacks the lungs and other parts of man's respiratory system, usually slowing down the cleaning action of the little hairlike structures—the cilia—that line the main parts of the system. It also can be a strong irritant to the eyes and skin. It can even destroy the enamel on teeth. And many of the effects of this gas on man are permanent and irreparable.

The most common source of this gas is the burning of oil and coal. Of course, various kinds of coal and oil have differing amounts of sulfur in them. The more sulfur there is, the more sulfur dioxide will result from the burning. For example, if coal with a high sulfur content is burned, as much as 10 percent of the weight of the coal may enter the atmosphere as sulfur dioxide gas. It is this gas that causes the "London-type" smog, and it was primarily responsible for the deaths mentioned earlier, not only in London, but also in Donora and in the Meuse Valley.

Doctors in Nashville blamed increases of asthma attacks on sulfur dioxide in the air. The gas also causes chronic catarrh, emphysema, shortness of breath, and even chronic fatigue. There may be a connection between this gas and heart trouble and anemia.

For every ton of coal that is burned, an average of eighty pounds of sulfur dioxide is released into the air. For every thousand gallons of gasoline burned in automobiles, an average of seventeen pounds of sulfur dioxide pollutes the atmosphere.

It is not always the sulfur dioxide that dirties the air which causes damage to man and his property. When the air is moist, some complicated chemical reactions occur between water and the oxides of sulfur. And the result is a sulfuric acid mist.

If these sulfur compounds can hurt man, they can affect animals, too. For the farmer, the effects of this type of pollution can have serious economic results because of the death of livestock.

Plants are damaged by sulfur dioxide and sulfuric acid. Around Kingston, Tennessee, within a twenty-mile radius of the town, 90 percent of the white pine trees have been killed. Scientists blame the sulfur dioxide from a Tennessee Valley Authority power plant for this condition.

Fifty years ago two copper smelters near Ducktown, Tennessee, released so much sulfur dioxide into the air that it poisoned the soil. Even today, the land is almost bare of vegetation.

A copper refinery in Carteret, New Jersey, for years

emitted sulfur dioxide fumes. And a New York City Health Department official said at the time: "Nobody in Carteret has a lawn. That's the saddest community you ever saw."

But damage to living things is not all. Sulfur dioxide and sulfuric acid in the air also cause damage to such things as metal, paint, and stone by eroding these materials. Nylon stockings can be almost completely dissolved by acid droplets in the air.

New York City has the dubious honor of being the town with the highest sulfur dioxide concentration in the United States, so you would expect to find an erosion problem there. One recent example of erosion was the dome of St. Luke's Hospital. It was made of marble and terra-cotta, and for years the sulfur dioxide had been taking its toll. The marble had been weakened so much that it crumbled between the fingers like sugar cubes. Finally, the dome was replaced by a flat roof.

Another gaseous air pollutant is carbon monoxide. Only one part in 100,000 will cause illness; one part in 750, death in 30 minutes. This gas, a mixture of carbon and oxygen, is most often associated with the exhaust gas that comes from automobiles. It is also the gas that is so well publicized in newspaper stories about people who commit suicide by letting their automobile engines run in closed garages and inhaling the fumes. Actually, carbon monoxide is not usually a serious pollutant in our atmosphere. In heavy concentrations it is, of course, poisonous. But most of the time the concentration of

Carbon monoxide can kill. The bare trees at the left are dying because of the exhaust gases from the vehicles that constantly stop at this corner

carbon monoxide in the air is not high enough to do any damage to human health.

For every thousand gallons of gasoline burned in automobile engines, about three thousand pounds of carbon monoxide are given off into the air. In spite of this large amount of gas, medical researchers said for years that carbon monoxide was not a dangerous gas when it is given off into the *open* air.

Lately, however, more scientific evidence is being found that should make us more suspicious of carbon monoxide—even in the open air. To begin with, carbon monoxide reduces the ability of the blood to carry oxygen. This means that there will be an additional strain on the blood-pumping function of the heart as more blood must be transported much more rapidly through the body. Also, strain is put on the respiratory system as it must bring more and more oxygen into the lungs.

In addition, there seems to be evidence that there is such a thing as chronic carbon monoxide poisoning—that is, while a human may not be killed by the gas, the effects of the poisoning may build up within the body. Some of the milder symptoms are nausea, weakness, headache, and dizziness. The effects of the gas can be stored in the bloodstream by making stable compounds with the hemoglobin, thereby preventing it from carrying the much-needed oxygen to other parts of the body. A heavy cigarette smoker has a head start on chronic carbon monoxide poisoning, since he may have as much as 5 percent of his hemoglobin in permanent combination with carbon monoxide.

Some scientists feel that many of the accidents on highways that have been blamed on fatigue were probably caused by carbon monoxide poisoning of a mild type.

The United States Public Health Service recently completed a test on office workers whose offices were within one hundred feet of heavily traveled streets in

New York City. The researchers found that because of the inability of the blood to carry sufficient oxygen to the brain, these workers were often becoming befuddled. In spite of the fact that they were working in a filtered, air-conditioned atmosphere—right in their offices—they were breathing air that had a concentration of carbon monoxide three times higher than the level at which mental processes can become affected. Since no one knew how well coordinated these workers were in a normal atmosphere, the effects of carbon monoxide poisoning were undetected for many years. This story points out that the filter on an air-conditioner cannot be used to keep out carbon monoxide.

Other gaseous pollutants, called smog reactants, usually begin as gases such as hydrocarbons (combinations of hydrogen and carbon) and oxides of nitrogen (oxygen plus nitrogen). They are products of incomplete burning in stoves, furnaces, and so on—but most of all in the automobile engine.

As you cruise along the highway at a constant speed, the engine of the car is pretty efficient. But in the city or on country roads, the picture changes. Every time you speed up or slow down, the engine loses much of its efficiency and the burning of the fuel is less complete. The next time you are in a car, watch the automobile ahead. Sometimes you will notice the visible exhaust gas come rolling out as the car pulls away from a stoplight or slows down at a corner.

At the same time that incomplete burning in the en-

Smog on a Los Angeles freeway, where the cause and the effect come together

gine is causing the hydrocarbons to enter the atmosphere from the exhaust pipe, something else is going on in the engine: it is releasing nitrogen oxides into the air. Then a complex chemical reaction occurs. In the presence of sunlight, the hydrocarbons combine with the oxides of nitrogen and the free oxygen in the air. The result is a large number of strange gases that cause the Los Angeles-type smog. This is also known as photochemical smog because it is caused by a chemical reaction in which sunlight is necessary.

One of the oxides of nitrogen—nitric oxide—reduces the oxygen-carrying ability of the blood. This reaction is the same as the one produced by carbon monoxide. Also, if it is concentrated enough, another substance, nitrogen dioxide, may injure the lungs. This last named oxide of nitrogen is a major cause of eye irritation when air pollution is above normal.

Nitrogen dioxide can also kill you. Several years ago, X-ray film in a Cleveland hospital caught fire, releasing a great deal of nitrogen dioxide into the air in the building. One hundred and twenty-five people were killed by the gas.

Hydrocarbons, the other most common smog reactants, come in many shapes and sizes. It has been said that exhaust fumes from automobiles contain about two hundred different kinds of these compounds. Almost twenty pounds come from the burning of one ton of coal. And some of these compounds are carcinogenic—they can cause cancer.

Let's take a look at one of them: benzopyrene. Evidence, not only in a United States Surgeon General's Report of 1964, but also from all over the world, shows that this hydrocarbon can cause cancer. It is one of the chemical compounds that come from cigarette smoke and is a producer of cancer of the lung. But it is not found only in cigarette smoke. Most of the benzopyrene in our air comes from coal fires; 10 percent of it comes from the exhaust gases of automobiles; some more of it comes from road tar and roof tar, oil fires, and processed rubber. Sometimes it is even eaten, having been found in oysters that came from polluted water.

In most cities, the mere act of breathing causes an individual to inhale as much benzopyrene as if he had smoked about seven cigarettes per day. A baby in New York City may at this very time be breathing in the equivalent of nine cigarettes per day. The scores for some other cities at the present time are: Cincinnati—26 cigarettes per day, Detroit—37, Nashville—40, and Birmingham—50. By the way, Birmingham, as you might expect, has the highest rate of lung cancer among the cities mentioned.

At least five other carcinogenic hydrocarbons are known to exist in polluted air.

Even as we breathe all this aerial garbage, something else may be going on—photochemical reactions. As you know, in the presence of sunlight, hydrocarbons and nitrogen oxides may form more complicated compounds. One of the most common of these compounds is PAN (peroxyacyl nitrate). This can cause the type of irritation to humans that we find in the Los Angeles-type smog.

And it can also kill plants. The citrus groves and truck farms in the Los Angeles area are not as productive as they once were. Orchids and spinach are almost vanished crops in the metropolitan area of Los Angeles.

Some plants, such as alfalfa, are not killed by PAN. Instead, they seem to store up this chemical. Then, when the plants are eaten by animals, PAN can cause a disease called fluorosis.

The last type of gaseous pollutant is the total oxidant. A very much simplified definition of oxidation is: the chemical combination of a substance with oxygen. And an oxidant is an oxidizing agent—a substance that provides the oxygen for oxidation. There is a rather complicated gas called ozone which is the most common product of total oxidation in our air.

Ozone is similar to oxygen in structure, but not in its properties. Oxygen, that gas so essential to life as we know it on this planet, is really made up of two atoms of oxygen combined together. In other words, if we could see the oxygen molecule, we would find that it consisted of two identical tinier particles, called atoms, of oxygen joined together. The reason why the oxygen molecule consists of two atoms rather than one is that the single oxygen atom is too highly reactive to exist alone for very long. So, if there were a single atom of oxygen around, it would readily combine with another to form a particle of oxygen gas, or with two atoms of hydrogen to form a particle of water, or with countless other types of atoms to form countless other substances.

But ozone, although composed of oxygen atoms only, is quite different from oxygen gas. Ozone is made up of three atoms of oxygen instead of two. It is sometimes formed by large quantities of energy in the form of electricity passing through oxygen, as when lightning strikes through the air. However, most of the ozone in our atmosphere is formed at great heights by the action of ultraviolet light from the sun on oxygen in the high-altitude atmosphere.

Most of the ozone so produced stays in the high reaches of the air. And we can consider ourselves lucky that it does. For one thing, it acts as a screen, filtering out some of the ultraviolet light that comes from the sun. As the ultraviolet light energy is absorbed by the ozone, it produces a layer of high temperature about thirty-five miles above the earth, forming a sort of blanket. Ozone also keeps much of the ultraviolet light from reaching living things. If humans were to be exposed to all of the ultraviolet light that enters our atmosphere, we would sunburn twice as fast and be very uncomfortable.

The second reason why we should be glad the ozone stays up there is that it is poisonous to living things. When concentrated, it can kill both plants and animals.

However, some ozone does get into the air we breathe. Some of it is brought to earth when the wind currents are just right. It can also be formed in the lower atmosphere in the same way as it is formed in the upper atmosphere.

Enough ozone gets to sea level to contribute to the Los Angeles-type smog. It is because of this that, in some areas of the world, the air is constantly being sampled to detect the presence of this gas. And in some places the ozone content of the air is the usual index of smog severity.

Ozone is probably the most serious pollutant of all the oxidants. Even if the concentration of the gas is not

high enough to kill, it can produce eye irritation, coughing, and chest soreness. It has been known to produce a
strange thickening of the lung tissues when it is inhaled
by animals in the laboratory.

Ozone affects green plants, too. It attacks the upper
half of their leaves, just under the skin, causing spotting.
Some of the most susceptible crops are grapes, alfalfa,
pineapple, wheat, peaches, corn, carrots, broccoli, beets,
spinach, strawberries, turnips, and potatoes. Obviously,
ozone damage is quite a problem for farmers.

This gas can also attack textiles—even to the point
of destroying the very dye used to color them—and it
also causes rubber to deteriorate. As a matter of fact, one
of the simplest ways to test for the ozone content in the
air is to stretch a piece of rubber tubing and see how long
it takes to crack. Of course, ozone also can have a great
effect on automobile tires.

But there is one more serious problem. This has to
do with the airplanes that usually fly in the upper atmosphere where the ozone concentration is naturally
higher. Ozone not only can affect airplane tires, but it
also can destroy the rubber used in sealing the windows
and in insulating the electrical wiring of the planes.

5

Radioactive and Miscellaneous Pollutants in the Air

No matter where in the world they live, all plants and animals are constantly being exposed to radioactive pollutants. They are continuously receiving cosmic radiation from outer space, and many organisms, both plant and animal, live in areas where radiation comes from radioactive ores in the earth. These sources constitute what is known as "background radiation."

In the more civilized areas of the world, living things pick up additional radiation from exposure to such sources as X-ray machines or even watch dials.

All of these sources, whether they are natural or created for the benefit of man, are permanent. And there is nothing that can be done about them; for if we could eliminate them, we would not, since we would be terribly inconvenienced.

Almost the only types of radioactive pollutants that we might care to eliminate if we could are those resulting from the testing of nuclear devices. There are ways to control the pollution resulting from this testing, but a thorough discussion of the subject would require more space than is available in this book, since it would involve not only science and technology, but also world politics.

We can learn to live with the natural background types of radioactivity. But when man-made radioactive substances pollute the air in high enough concentration, they can destroy living things. Actually, if the air is sufficiently polluted with these substances, death comes quickly both to animals and to plants.

Even in lesser concentrations, atomic radiation can be quite serious. Here is one example: on an atoll in the Pacific Ocean in 1954, a nuclear bomb was exploded. The name of this atoll was Bikini, and it was the test site for atomic explosions that were to be studied by American scientists. Miles away, on another atoll called Rongelap, eighty-two natives were living peaceful lives. The wind, carrying the radioactive pollution from the Bikini blast, suddenly shifted and headed straight for Rongelap. Immediately an American research team speeded to Rongelap and was able to evacuate the whole island within forty-eight hours after the fallout hit the atoll. Even though the fallout concentration was diluted by its trip over the ocean, within ten days most of the natives showed evidence of radioactive burns. More than ten years later, some of them were still developing symptoms of radioactive poisoning. Some had lumps in their thyroid glands, pigmented moles, and other abnormal conditions. To be specific, eighteen of the eighty-two now have thyroid problems, and ten of these eighteen developed their conditions years after the fallout. There is no telling where this story will end, but it is interesting to note that none of the natives who were among the first to be rescued have developed any of these thyroid abnormalities.

Since there is very little that can be done about nuclear reactions that produce radioactive fallout, save banning nuclear testing aboveground, a great deal of care must be taken in the disposal of radioactive wastes. These wastes usually come from such operations as mines containing radioactive materials, refineries or processing plants that use these materials, nuclear reactors, nuclear power plants, and so on.

One scientist has estimated that sometime in the mid-1970's about fifty-six thousand gallons of radioactive waste will have been disposed of. By the mid-1990's, the waste will have increased to about three hundred million gallons, which, he estimates, will have the radioactive energy of about sixty-five billion grams, or about one hundred forty-three million pounds, of radium.

This waste keeps much of its energy, and it may take more than one thousand years from the disposal date for it to become harmless to life. As long as radioactive substances keep giving off radiation particles, they are potentially dangerous. Strontium 90, for example, may take as long as twenty-five years to give off half of its radiation, and radium takes one thousand six hundred and twenty-two years to give off half of its radiation.

Since this waste can be dangerous, it must be stored. It can't be burned. It can't be eliminated by the addition of chemicals. So the best place to store it is where it will not come in contact with living things for centuries. Putting the waste in tanks, as once was done, then throwing the tanks into the ocean, is a bad idea. The tanks may rust and release the waste into the ocean water.

One storage method being investigated is the injection of the waste into a deep sandstone layer under the earth. Sandstone is so spongelike that it can absorb the waste, though only in liquid form. The Oak Ridge National Laboratory in Tennessee is injecting radioactive waste materials into shale beds underground. The waste is first mixed with cement and other substances and then pumped underground to depths of from seven hundred to one thousand feet. After a time, the conglomeration hardens, and thus is safely stored away for centuries to come. Another, and similar, method is one in which the waste material is solidified in phosphate glass. Still another method is the deposit of wastes in unused salt mines.

Whatever the method used, the waste must be disposed of where the containers will not erode or rust away, where living things are not found, and where such geological phenomena as earthquakes will not accidentally expose the material. We don't yet have the perfect answer —not with those three hundred million gallons in our future.

All the rest of the air pollutants fall in the category of miscellaneous pollutants. Of these substances two are probably the most common. The first is carbon dioxide. This is the gas that is given off by most living things in the process called respiration. In humans, for example, it is the waste product of breathing. Although green plants also give off a certain amount of this gas in respiration, they also take it in to be used as a raw material in photosynthesis, the process by which green plants manufacture their own food—simple sugar.

Since 1900 there has been an increase in the carbon dioxide concentration in our atmosphere. The reason for this is that our use of the so-called "fossil fuels"—coal, oil, and gasoline—has increased during this century. At the present time, however, we don't have to worry too much about this. Not that carbon dioxide could not become a problem, but at least it is not the most serious pollutant in the air, since it does dissolve rapidly in water and is taken in by green plants.

Carbon dioxide also absorbs some of the heat that is radiated from the earth. In one way this is convenient, since it prevents the escape of some of this heat into outer space. But if the concentration of the gas were to increase a great deal, it would have an effect on the temperature of our atmosphere.

This is what may happen in the future. If we keep destroying green plants to build cities and highways, we will be eliminating the living things that take in carbon dioxide and give off oxygen. If we increase our burning of fossil fuels, we increase the amount of carbon dioxide in the air. The result of this action is a rise in the carbon dioxide in the atmosphere.

Carbon dioxide does absorb heat radiation and trap it in the air, and it also is colorless—permitting the sun's rays to reach the earth. Therefore, if the concentration of the carbon dioxide rises, so does the amount of heat energy trapped in the earth's atmosphere.

If, over a period of many years, the concentration keeps rising, the temperature of our whole planet could rise gradually. If it kept on rising, it is possible that the polar ice caps could melt. Catastrophes could occur all along the coastlines all over the world.

Carbon dioxide has its effects on nonliving things, too. Some stone buildings—particularly those made of limestone—have, over the years, been eaten away by carbonic acid. If there is a high concentration of carbon dioxide in the air, plus a high degree of moisture in the atmosphere, the result can be a chemical reaction producing this acid. The stone will be discolored and weakened. Finally, when it rains, the water may wash away the surface of the stone.

The other common type of miscellaneous pollutant can be called the aeroallergen. These substances come in all shapes and sizes and produce a wide variety of effects. They are pollutants carried in the air that cause allergic reactions in some animals and some plants.

Many persons are allergic to some types of pollutants, although most of us have no reactions to these substances. A common example is the pollutant that affects huge numbers of humans every summer—the ragweed pollen which causes hay fever. There are other, more exotic diseases, such as silo-fillers disease—a reaction to dust from grain—and farmer's lung—a sensitivity to moldy vegetable dust or fertilizer.

And some of us are abnormally allergic to many of the other kinds of pollutants—that is, an unusual reaction occurs when we breathe in pollutants of various kinds, even in low concentrations which would not normally disturb other people. Some scientists think that many people suffer from car sickness not because of the motion of the automobile but because of an allergic reaction to mild amounts of car exhaust gases.

Dr. Theron G. Randolph of the Swedish Covenant Hospital in Chicago tells of people who became ill after driving through an area containing refineries, steel mills, and chemical and paint manufacturing plants. "Some noticed only mucous membrane irritation. Others became nervous, jittery, irritable." They developed a wide range of allergic reactions: hay fever symptoms, asthma-like attacks, fatigue, and headaches. Some appeared to be drunk.

6

Smokestacks and Automobiles

Years ago, Pittsburgh was laughingly called "The Smoky City" by the rest of the country. But the people of Pittsburgh were not laughing. Smoke from the steel mills and the coal-burning steam trains blackened everything it touched. Even the street signs were sometimes so filthy that they could not be read. During the worst month recorded, two hundred and ninety-one tons of particles per square mile were dumped on the streets, buildings, and people.

Finally, in 1945, plans were made for doing something about the filth. Smoke control laws were passed, and in just four years a wonderful change was seen. Pittsburgh was no longer "The Smoky City."

All over the world, devices have been developed and laws have been passed that will cut down on the pollution from chimneys. Some industries have altered their production so particles can be trapped before they are given off into the atmosphere only to discover that they can turn in a higher profit because they have cut down on pollution. Some have sold the fly ash that they captured to cement companies, who use it in certain products. Other industries trapped sulfur dioxide and were able to reuse it in their laboratories.

Natural gas is much less of a polluter than coal or fuel oil, since it emits almost no sulfur dioxide. The Air Pollution Control Commission of the state of New Jersey has proposed that the industry of the state convert to fuels containing less sulfur. They suggest a fuel that will release into the atmosphere less than two thousand parts per million of sulfur dioxide, and that all new factories being built should use fuel which will release less than five hundred parts per million.

In New York, St. Vincent's Hospital has erected a device that sprays water into the smoke from their heating plant. The particles plus the water produce a sludge that can be collected in barrels. The hospital officials claim that the method is almost 100 percent efficient and that they are getting a yield of about three-quarters of a barrel of sludge per day.

The Long Island Railroad, although it does have many miles of electrified track, still has many diesel trains. The management, however, is thinking of testing a battery-powered train to reduce air pollution.

The real problems of changing from one fuel to another are cost and availability. Although it may cost a great deal of money to convert, often this is not the main reason why industry does not do so. Large-scale use of atomic power may be possible in another ten years, but the fuel is not readily obtained now. For one thing, until 1964 there was a law that all special nuclear materials had to be owned by the federal government. For another, until 1966 more nuclear materials were needed for weapons than for peaceful uses. And 1967 marked the year in which the Atomic Energy Commission first began to give "serious consideration" to selling or leasing one of their atomic energy plants to industry. Atomic fuel use is still in its infancy.

While it would be nice if everyone switched to low-sulfur fuels, the supply is limited. Natural gas may be unavailable. Many cities do not have enough waterpower to run electric generating plants. So, for many polluting industries, a cure is not possible.

But how about garbage? Everybody has a supply of this commodity. New York City's Air Pollution Control Commissioner, Austin N. Heller, has made the suggestion that industry stoke its boilers with garbage. Garbage is a non-sulfurous fuel and is readily available. The city's garbage could supply about one-quarter of New York's power needs per year. Garbage that is now being dumped into such places as marshes would be burned instead and the marshes could continue to support their normal quota of fish, birds, and other wildlife.

Garbage-burning for industry and power plants is not a new idea, though. In Europe, except for Great Britain, most large garbage incinerators built since World War II have used the heat produced by the fires for power. Every ton of refuse burned yields about one hundred forty kilowatt-hours of electricity. By 1969, 7 percent of the electrical power used by the city of Amsterdam will be generated from garbage. The Norfolk

(Virginia) Naval Base is experimenting with a steam-producing garbage incinerator in which each ton of garbage will yield more than three tons of steam.

Los Angeles had such an air pollution problem that, as we know, a type of smog was named after it. Automobiles were contributing up to 65 percent of the pollution to the atmosphere. Inversions were holding the pollution over the city, and the famous California sunshine was causing photochemical effects. In the 1940's, concerned people were even suggesting that tunnels be dug through the mountains and that fans be installed in the tunnels to suck the smog out of Los Angeles. Others suggested that giant mirrors be set up to reflect the sun's rays, heat the air, and thus carry off the smog with rising air currents.

But eventually, in 1947, an air pollution control board was formed, and then began one of the most widespread campaigns against air pollution in history. The board had the authority to control pollution anywhere in Los Angeles County—an area of some four thousand square miles, or about the size of four Rhode Islands, two Delawares, or one Connecticut. The board immediately set up regulations to limit air pollution from industry by prohibiting the use of high-sulfur fuels, open-air burning of garbage, or the burning of junked automobiles. The laws even forbade the sale of such things as smog-forming chemicals in larger than one-quart containers, and they set standards for the permissible amount of poisonous solvents in house paint.

The board not only began to abolish coal burning,

The trouble with outdoor incineration is that it can cause pollution for miles around

but also forbade the burning of fuel oil in all but five months in the year. They outlawed all backyard incinerators. The result was that the amount of pollution in the air of Los Angeles was reduced from six thousand three hundred and seventy-five tons per day to thirteen hundred and seventy-five tons per day. This figure is amazing, but the board realized that the new low figure is merely equal to the amount of pollution found in the city in 1940. And Angelinos were disturbed by the amount of pollution in the air then, too. The war was not over.

The fight went on. Thousands of pollution violators were taken to court. When an oil company was convicted of polluting the air, such was the support of the board by the citizens of Los Angeles that fifteen hundred people canceled the credit cards which were issued by this company. The board closed down, in one single day, fifty-eight million dollars' worth of incinerators. Now the city has the least offensive industries in the world. But the smog is still there. In fact, it is getting worse, because more and more people are moving in who are driving more and more automobiles.

The state of California passed the first law in this country which required all cars, from 1964 models on, to have devices that would send unburned gasoline back into the engine to be burned. All cars from 1966 models on would have to be equipped with a device that would reduce the carbon monoxide in the exhaust gas by 50 percent and the hydrocarbons by 65 percent. The law also provides for further reduction in exhaust pollutants by 1970, as new techniques are developed to do this job.

These laws are not enough, however. In the first place, it takes about ten years to eliminate old cars from the road. So it will be 1974 or 1976 before most of the California cars without these devices are in junkyards. In the second place, it has been found that the devices themselves lose efficiency as the automobile is driven. The more miles on the car, the more pollution in the air.

Automobile makers have, for many years, been working on ways to improve the efficiency of the internal combustion engine and lower the pollutants that come out of the engine, the crankcase, and the exhaust. They have spent millions of dollars developing antipollution systems. Some of these systems were complete failures, while some of them have been moderately successful.

To begin with, it is theoretically possible to have an automobile that is a low-level polluter. If the engine of an auto with precision parts under the hood is kept in fine tune, it should be acceptable. The level of pollutants given off would be under the level set by the state of California. But how many people would keep their engines in fine tune? And how much would it cost to do so? And how could the owners of defective automobiles be detected? Clearly, this is not the answer.

One of the early alternative proposals was to clean up the exhaust by inserting a chemical into the exhaust system that would act as a catalyst. This chemical would decompose the pollution compounds and trap the more serious poisons. A chemical called vanadium pentoxide was discovered to be effective. However, when the packet of vanadium pentoxide became clogged with pollutants, it was no longer usable and had to be replaced or the auto would give off as much pollution as if the packet were not there.

A method was developed by which afterburners were used to burn the exhaust gas before it hit the outside air. This involved the insertion of a spark plug into the exhaust system. The spark from the plug would then set fire to the exhaust gases and unburned fuel. It also involved the connection of part of the car's electrical system to the rear of the engine and the additional cost of changing an extra spark plug.

Two other methods of burning the unburned fuel are now being tested. One is the pumping of air into the exhaust system near the exhaust valves. The temperature at this point is high enough to burn the unburned fuel when it mixes with the air. This has some drawbacks. It adds extra heat under the hood, and some engineers fear that the wear and tear on the exhaust system will be too much for the car to take.

The other method being tested involves the pumping of more air into the engine along with the fuel, which results in more efficient burning. This, in addition to a more efficiently shaped combustion chamber, eliminates much of the pollution from the automobile. The advantage of this method is that the extra burning occurs in the combustion chamber, where the additional heat will improve the engine's performance, rather than in the exhaust system, where it becomes something of an afterthought.

In January of 1967, however, a discouraging word came from pollution experts in California. Forty percent of the 1966 California automobiles equipped with the new devices failed the smog test. In fact, autos that had been driven more than twenty thousand miles had a failure rate of 87 percent.

Los Angeles County expects two million more automobiles to be on its roads by 1980. Add all of this up and it turns out that unless the pollution control devices are greatly improved, the pollution and the smog will increase. This is especially true when we know that a car sitting in the sun produces, by evaporation, almost as much hydrocarbon pollution as if it were being driven.

Some scientists are concerned about another problem having to do with these control devices. Even if something could be done to eliminate all the hydrocarbons from automobile exhaust, the cars would still be pouring nitrogen oxides into the air, and the cure might be worse than the disease. At least now these two chemicals combine photochemically to produce smog, and we have a shaky and unpleasant balance. But if the hydrocarbons disappear, we may be poisoned by the nitrogen oxide remaining. The Atlantic Richfield Oil Company has been working, since 1960, on the development of another device—one that will cut down on nitrogen oxide fumes.

But what about automobile exhaust? General Motors is testing a gas turbine bus that will produce only 10 percent of the exhaust pollution now released by buses. It runs on kerosine, just as the engines in jet aircraft do, and has only 20 percent of the number of moving parts that a diesel bus has. This cuts down on the pollution coming from lubricating oils, too. The engine is lighter than the usual bus engine. The only problem is the horrible noise. If that can't be muffled, we may have to trade one type of pollution for another—air pollution for noise pollution.

Some automotive engineers in Detroit are working on an exhaust device that will cut hydrocarbons down to fifty parts per million. This figure is less than 20 percent of the allowable amount set by the federal government for the exhaust gases in all 1968 automobiles.

Scientists have developed antiozones, or substances that will remove ozone from the air. This is done by means of a chemical reaction. But there is one drawback. The antiozone is used up as it reacts with the ozone in the air. This means that the antiozone must continually be replaced—a very costly operation.

Obviously, the problem is becoming almost insoluble. There are many who feel that the answer to the automobile pollution problem lies in the development of a practical electric car. In fact, the major automobile manufacturers have sent their designers back to the drawing board—the same drawing board that the designers left decades ago when the electric automobile lost its popularity race with the gasoline engine.

In the early days of the motorcar, there was a furious race for the motorist's dollar. At that time, the big three in automobile manufacturing were the gasoline, steam, and electric car producers. Even then, the electric cars were more appealing because of their clean operation and the fact that their motors were almost completely silent.

To start the gasoline engine, the driver had to use a crank—resulting in frustration, bruised fingers, and an occasional broken arm. To start the steam engine, a boiler had to be fired up—resulting in frustration, burned fingers, and lost time. But the electric? Just jump in and drive away. You can imagine that this was a boon to lady drivers.

Electric automobiles were also smoother in their acceleration. There was no shifting of gears. They were less complicated, having fewer moving parts—no boiler, no transmission.

For years the electric was *the* fashionable car. Queen Victoria, Presidents Taft, Wilson, Harding, and Coolidge, all owned at least one. More than eighty different companies in the United States alone manufactured them at one time or another.

In 1925, however, came the downfall of the electric. In that year the electric self-starter was invented and put on the gasoline car, eliminating the crank.

By this time the steam car had been almost forgotten, but what caused the demise of the electric? First of all, the gasoline car always had been more maneuverable. Some of the electrics weighed almost three tons, about four-fifths of that weight being batteries. This meant that the lighter gasoline cars could travel over roads which could not accommodate an electric. And, if you ran out of electricity on a lonely road, where could you get a refill? So, once the necessity for cranking the gas buggy was eliminated, it won the race.

But according to a recent Gallup Poll, thirty-six million Americans would like to buy an electric car, and we may be seeing its return to the road. Such leaders as John R. MacGregor, speaking as the president of the American Society of Automotive Engineers, have warned: "This problem [of pollution by gasoline engines] must soon be solved or automotive power plants and their fuels, as we know them today, may go the way of the buggy whip. . . . By soon, I mean something like eight to ten years in Los Angeles, and twenty to twenty-five years in most metropolitan areas in the United States."

The Ford Motor Company has developed a new type of battery to replace the lead-acid battery. It is a sodium-sulfur device which will store about fifteen times more electricity per pound than the old-fashioned lead-acid battery. General Motors has an auto in an experimental stage that will run eighty miles on one charge of its silver-zinc battery. This company has also produced a lithium-air battery, which may give the car a range of one hundred miles. The Edison Electric Institute has developed a zinc-air battery which will give large delivery trucks from eighty to one hundred twenty miles of city driving without recharging. Westinghouse is working on an in-town compact car system.

These new developments add weight, of course. And cost. The silver-zinc battery, for example, weighs eight hundred pounds and costs thirty thousand dollars. Besides, it must be recharged more often than a gasoline tank must be filled.

The president of General Motors, Edward Cole, has

estimated that it will be late in the 1980's before all the bugs can be worked out of the mass production of electric cars. In the meantime, Congressman Richard Ottinger, of Pleasantville, New York, has had a Renault Dauphine equipped with five silver-zinc batteries and a 7.2 horsepower motor. The automobile will go as fast as fifty-five miles per hour and travel for seventy miles before it needs an eight-hour charge.

A breakthrough may be in sight, however. Electric Fuel Propulsion, Inc., is planning to go into mass production of an electric car early in 1969. Their car, called the Mars II, will sell for about $5,500, and the price may be even lower once the sales justify a reduction in cost. It will be powered by a lead-cobalt battery which will be much less expensive than the silver-zinc battery. The Mars II will have a range of one hundred twenty miles and should be able to hit sixty miles per hour. The manufacturers predict that eventually they can build a car which will have a range of two hundred forty miles and a speed of eighty miles per hour. The company plans to set up dealerships in the ten largest cities of the United States.

Some experts, however, have high hopes for the fuel cell. This is the device that supplies electricity to the capsules in our manned space programs. But fuel cells, too, are heavy and costly, in spite of their ability to produce electricity for long periods of time. Actually, they can continue to produce electricity as long as they are supplied with oxygen and a fuel such as hydrogen.

7

The Fight Goes On

For centuries, natural processes of air purification were enough to control air pollution. Snow and rain washed the pollutants out of the air. Much of the solid pollution matter merely fell to the ground to be absorbed into the soil. The slightly polluted air was cleaned as it filtered through vegetation.

A dramatic example of natural pollution control was observed during a severe blizzard in Chicago on January 26, 1967. Twenty-three inches of snow fell on that day, causing many industries and all schools to close. In addition, traffic was at a standstill. For three days, two of the most dangerous polluters—automobiles and industrial fires—gave off very little pollution. This, coupled with the washing of the air by the snow, resulted in a 90 percent drop in gaseous pollution and a 35 percent drop in solid pollution. But this pollution decrease lasted for only a short while and was due to extraordinary circumstances.

Man must begin to control his own pollution. And he has.

Scientists feel that there are only three general

Chicago on a smoggy day

methods by which air pollution can be reduced. The first is to change the fuels we use. For example, fuel oil produces less soot and fly ash than soft coal, and natural gas produces even less than fuel oil.

Another way to reduce pollution is to take advantage of the technology that has been developed in other fields.

Atomic power produces none of the solid or gaseous pollutants that other fuels do. Of course, it produces its own unique type of pollution, but that can be controlled if we use the proper precautions.

The third method is to keep on using the fuels we now use but to remove the pollutants before they can pollute the air. Devices have been developed to remove the solid particles and many of the undesirable gases from chimney smoke and automobile exhausts. Equipping every home chimney with these devices would be a bit of a problem, however.

The front line in the fight against the effects of air pollution is manned by the scientists and technicians who study the air and its unpleasant particles and gases. These men also are the people who must give information to the citizen on how to correct aerial garbage problems. Here are a few of the scientific studies that have been or are being carried out.

First of all, if a scientist is to study what is in the air, he must have some means of testing the amount of pollutant material in the air. There are several ways to measure the fine particles in the sky, but the smaller the particles, the harder they are to capture.

One of the most common ways of measuring the amount of particulate matter is to use a filtering method. Just as the coffee basket in the coffee percolator holds back the solid particles of coffee and lets the water through, so the scientists' filters hold back the solid particles of soot and let the air through.

The research scientist selects a filter to fit the size of

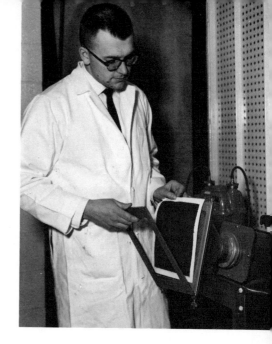

Filters are used to capture air-pollution sediment, which will then be analyzed

particle he wants to trap. If he wants to catch all of the solid particles in the air, he must run the air through a filter that has very small holes. If he wants to catch only the largest particles, he might select a filter with holes as large as four-one hundred thousandth of an inch across. That sounds small, but it is really large, as filter holes go.

Next, a known amount of air is pumped through the filter. The particles on the filter are removed, analyzed, and weighed. One easy way to weigh the collected material, since the weight of the filter is already known, is to weigh the filter containing the particles and then subtract the weight of the filter when it was clean. It is important to use the smallest quantity of polluted air that can be conveniently measured. If too much is used, the filter holes tend to clog. The more air, the more particles, and the greater chance of clogging and ruining the whole measurement. This is especially true when working with filters with the smaller holes—on the order of one-two hundred fifty thousandth of an inch.

When the particles are viewed under the microscope, many of them can be identified by their size, shape, crystal type, or color. Others must be tested with chemicals.

Another common method of measuring particles is the use of a settling device. Slides or jars are placed in locations where measurements are desired and are left there for a month or so. Sometimes the slides or jars are coated with a sticky substance that will trap the particles. When enough time has elapsed, the particles are weighed and analyzed. This is a convenient technique for testing the pollution fallout from certain factory areas: the scientists simply place jars or slides downwind of the fallout and wait.

It is obvious, however, that this method provides a measurement of fallout only per day, week, or month—not the amount of particulate matter per cubic meter of air. But a box can be rigged up and the collection jars and slides placed inside. Then a given volume of air can be pumped in. After the particles have settled, the jars, slides, and the insides of the box can be studied.

Another very accurate measuring technique can be used to sample the larger particles—those that are bigger than one-fifty thousandth of an inch. A device, called an impactor, pumps air through a nozzle at high speed. Different sizes of nozzles can be used, depending on the size of the particles to be captured. The air strikes a glass or plastic microscope slide and the speed of the air makes it bounce off the slide in all directions. The larger particles, being heavier than the air particles, stick to the slide, especially if it has been coated with something sticky. At the same time, the smaller pollution particles, weighing less, are carried away by the airstream.

Sometimes a strip of paper on a rolling drum is substituted for the microscope slide. As the strip is unrolled, differences in particle concentration can be seen, depending on the shades of gray the particles have left on the paper.

Three-stage impactors have been built, too. The first slide catches the larger particles. Then the air current is sent through a nozzle of smaller size onto a slide that captures the middle-sized particles. Finally, the air current is sent through an even smaller nozzle onto a slide that traps the smallest particles.

Still another type of impactor has been developed that uses an extremely fine spider web thread instead of a slide. This permits the trapping of very small particles.

There are other, more complicated, collecting devices. Some of them cause the particle-laden air to come in contact with microscope slides by means of hot and cold plates. The hot and cold plates are placed side by side, and the microscope slide is attached to the cold plate. As the air passes between the plates, the heat from the hot plate forces the polluted air toward the cold plate, where the pollutants attach themselves to the microscope slide.

Other devices use the magnetic properties of electricity to force the air in certain directions. There are also measuring devices that use a light beam and a photoelectric cell to record cloud densities of particulates.

Once the technician has the equipment and the know-how, it is relatively easy to measure and identify solid particles. It is not so easy to do the same for the gases that pollute the air.

One of the most common techniques for measuring and identifying gaseous pollutants is referred to as "scrubbing" the air. In this method, the air is passed through certain liquids that remove specific gases from the air. Scientists know of liquids that will remove sulfur dioxide, while other liquids take out hydrogen sulfide, et cetera. When the gas has been absorbed by the liquid, it can be measured.

Air can also be passed through filters, such as activated charcoal, which will adsorb the pollutants. The filter is then heated so that the pollutant is driven off to be measured and analyzed.

Monitoring machines have been developed that provide a constant measurement of many of the inorganic gases in the air. Some of these gases are sulfur dioxide, nitric oxide, nitrogen dioxide, and ozone. Some machines measure certain hydrocarbons; some measure other organic gases. The problem is, with regard to compounds containing carbon, that these devices usually measure almost all of them at once and cannot discriminate one carbon compound from another.

Who measures air pollution? One group concerned

with the problem is the public health agencies, such as the United States Public Health Service, state departments of health, and regional and city departments of health. This work is also done in college or university laboratories—especially those with medical schools or departments of public health. Then there is the nongovernmental or noncollege agency, such as the National Tuberculosis Association and the Travelers Research Center, that supports research. And there are private laboratories, not financed by any of the agencies mentioned, that gather data. All of these agencies cooperate.

One of the basic research problems in air pollution is the need for more knowledge about weather. After the pollutants get into the air, they may affect human beings hundreds of miles away. We must know which way the wind is blowing.

A group of scientists in Illinois has developed a method of monitoring polluted winds, using gamma rays from an atomic reactor. They believe that if a substance which produces gamma radiation is placed in a tube standing on end, the rays will go straight up into the air for several hundreds of feet, mixing and drifting with the polluted air. The mildly radioactive air, as it drifts, can be picked up on radar screens. If these radiation tubes are set up throughout a city and in the surrounding countryside, information on wind direction can be fed into a central computer. The "cure," if not properly controlled, may turn out to be worse than the disease, since further air pollution may be produced by radioactivity.

Scientists in England, at the Warren Spring Laboratory, Sevenage, Hertfordshire, have been studying smoke travel patterns in Cambridge and Bedford. By placing measuring devices on lamp posts within a radius of one-half mile from the major source of smoke pollution, and placing other measuring devices on balloons suspended at a height of five hundred feet within a radius of one mile from the source, they have discovered a strange fact. The smoke tends to leapfrog over areas of dense population. So, by learning more about smoke patterns, they find that they really know less about the way smoke is distributed over a city.

Not all current research is so discouraging, however. Some things are being tried that may lead to better control over industrial and home sources of air pollution.

Some scientists at the Academy of Science in Yerevan, Armenia, have discovered a new method for disposing of the soot that comes out of industrial smokestacks. With a blast of hydrogen gas, they spray the soot into a large cylinder, heat the mixture to a high temperature, and add pressures equal to ten thousand times the sea level air pressure on earth. The carbon of the soot combines with the hydrogen in such a way as to eliminate the pollutant and, at the same time, form acetylene, the valuable industrial gas that is used in acetylene torches. Not only have these men removed a pollutant: they also have made it pay.

West Germany is losing forest trees because of smoke damage from aluminum-producing factories. Scientists at the Bavarian Forestry Research Institute have taken cuttings from the few spruce trees that have been able to withstand the smoke and have grafted the cuttings onto other trees. The result has been some cultivated trees that can live through as much as three times the normal concentrations of industrial sulfur dioxide.

Many factories all over the world have installed electrostatic filters to remove dust particles from their waste gases. But if these dust particles are not electrically charged, they cannot be removed in this way. To overcome this problem, researchers at the Research Institute of Siemens-Schuckertwerke in Erlangen, West Germany, have developed a new technique. They whirl the waste gases in an artificial tornado. The solid particles, because of their weight, are thrown through the tornado, toward the outside. They then pass through tubes and are flushed into containers. Instead of going into the air, the particles go to the garbage dump.

From the Hobo Science Laboratory in Kamakura, Japan, came an example of cooperation between biologists and chemists who were searching for a way to reduce the amount of sulfurous acid and sulfuric acid gases in the smoke from the burning of petroleum. Biologists found an enzyme that was extracted from microbes, and the chemists injected this enzyme into the petroleum. Not only were the acid gases removed, but also the burning of the fuel was made more efficient. The former ugly brown gas coming out of the chimney became transparent in from ten to fifteen minutes after the use of the enzyme. Biologists are still trying to discover the chemical nature of the enzyme. Perhaps it can be made artificially.

Another treatment for the removal of sulfur dioxide from coal smoke is being tested. The fuel is mixed with chips of dolomitic rock and then subjected to very high temperatures. Dolomitic rock is similar to limestone and contains calcium magnesium carbonate. The dolomite removes the sulfur from the fuel, and no sulfur dioxide can be formed when the fuel burns. Then the sulfur can be removed from the rock and used by chemists. The rock itself can be reused in this process.

Scientists in many places are suggesting that plants can serve as pollution detectors. As you know, plants vary in their reactions to different gases. At the Southwestern Forest Experimental Station in Asheville, North Carolina, pine seedlings have been tested for their responses to fluorine gas, sulfur dioxide, and ozone. Tests at the University of Delaware revealed that spinach, tobacco, cultivated dock, annual bluegrass, and pine trees can be used as ozone detectors. Also, snapdragons and carnations are affected by ethylene; tomatoes and some alfalfas by sulfur dioxide; grapes and peaches by fluorine; and petunias, spinach, lamb's-quarters, and cultivated dock by peroxacyl peroxide. Dr. Robert H. Daines, a plant pathologist at Rutgers, has discovered that orchids and carnations are susceptible to ethylene, and this gas also causes tomato plants to bend downward and outward.

So plants can be used as canaries once were used in coal mines. When the canaries started to flutter around, the miners knew there might be some poisonous gas in the mine because the birds were more sensitive than humans to some gases. Now scientists are suggesting that we watch the plants. When some begin to die, there may be an excess of certain pollutants in the air.

Then there is the cancer problem. Researchers have been suspicious of pollution as a cancer-causing agent since 1924. In that year, Dr. J. Meyers of the New York City Department of Health made the first study revealing the connection between air pollution and cancer of the lung. Of course, there are now so many cancer research projects being carried on that we could not possibly know of them all. Therefore, let us consider just one as an example of what has been done.

A group of scientists at the Pasadena (California) Foundation for Medical Research found that there may be a connection between some types of fine particle pollution and cancer in addition to the connection between some gases and lung cancer. They filtered ordinary air from over the city and separated out the particle pollutants. Then they added these particles to a group of living cells in a tissue culture. Some of the cells in the culture reacted just as if they were reacting to a carcinogen. Then the researchers took air that was more heavily polluted with automobile exhaust gases. This air was washed until the water used also contained the pollutants. A tissue culture of living cells from the inner surface of a human eyelid was prepared, and the water was added to the culture. Some of the human cells grew bigger; some of them divided more rapidly than usual; some divided into unusual shapes. The cells were behaving like cancer cells. A number of the fine particles appeared to have been carcinogens.

Research is going on in the field of radiation pollution, too. At Cornell University, Willard J. Visek and Hung Chen Dang have been trying to give radiation immunity to mice. They injected urease, a type of enzyme, into the mice, and these animals developed antibodies that reduced their production of ammonia. The scientists then exposed many mice, both treated and untreated, to a high-level dose of cobalt gamma rays. Thirty percent of the untreated mice died. Only 8 percent of the treated mice died. The immunity to radiation lasted for weeks, and, in some cases, months. Apparently the radioactivity immunity of the mice was built up, but the scientists do not yet know how.

Even the effects of air pollution due to salt are being examined. The air in Venice, Italy, has a great deal of this kind of pollution. And the bronze horses on top of the main portal of San Marco's in Venice are beginning to show the effects of the salt in the air. Chemists are working on the development of a protective solution to coat the horses with. They are being spurred on perhaps by an old saying in this Italian city: "When the horses come down, Venice will fall."

This, then, has been a sampling of the kinds of unfinished research now being carried out. Results are tentative, but the work goes on. Technologists and lawmakers have done a great deal with the findings of research. According to a former Surgeon General of the United States, Dr. Luther L. Terry, "almost all kinds of air pollution can be overcome. We have the techniques. And now we must do the job."

8

At What a Cost

One fact must be faced. Stamping out air pollution is not going to be cheap. However, when we consider that a normal, healthy person can live about five weeks without food and five days without water, but only five minutes without air, it may be well worth the price.

Many big businesses have been spending large sums on pollution control. For example, General Motors is said to have put more than thirty million dollars into research on cleaning up the gasoline engine, and the job has not been finished yet. The electric power industries have spent about seven hundred fifty million dollars, and the oil industries some two hundred fifty million in the last ten years alone. It is estimated that the chemical manu-facturers spend forty-three million per year, and that the steel industry's outlays in Chicago alone total about six million dollars annually.

The reports of expenditures by local governments are rather spotty. To begin with, the United States Public Health Service has recommended that about fifty cents per person per year might clear up most of our air pollution problems. But in areas where there are pollution-control agencies, only about one in seven is spending even as much as thirty-five cents per person.

Part of Cook County, Illinois, heads the list, with more than eighty-three cents per resident. This is the county in which Chicago is located, but the figure given is for the county *minus* Chicago. The money spent by the larger cities ranges from less than sixteen cents per person in New York City to more than sixty cents in Los Angeles.

What does the public get for its money? It seems to get what it pays for. Until 1967, New York City's pollution measurements were all carried on in one ten-foot square room in a Harlem courthouse. The room had one window and contained instruments for measuring carbon dioxide, carbon monoxide, and smoke—but those pollutants were measured only as they were found in the air outside that one window. The staff of the New York Department of Air Pollution Control numbered twenty-seven. It has since been increased and has been given better facilities.

Los Angeles' pollution-control budget, being almost four million dollars per year, permits a great deal of activity. The Los Angeles County Air Pollution Control District employs a staff of two hundred eighty-four, rings up a total of two hundred twenty-five thousand inspections, and issues seventy thousand operating permits per year. Even considering this hectic pace, these men have reduced air pollution to only about the 1940 level.

It isn't logical to feel smug about the fact that state

agencies in the United States spend a total of about two million two hundred thousand dollars per year on air pollution control. More than half of that amount is spent by the state of California alone. Local agencies spend over four million dollars per year, but Los Angeles accounts for almost half of this outlay. The story is rather sad. Even as recently as 1961, only seventeen of the fifty states spent as much as five thousand dollars per year on the solving of this problem.

When we talk about such huge amounts of money, it is easy to forget how much this means to the average person. In Pittsburgh sixty years ago—smoky as it was—the cost of air pollution control per person was only about twenty dollars per year because prices were lower and there were fewer automobiles at that time. During the past half century, however, the number of registered automobiles has grown at a staggering rate. In Connecticut alone the number of registrations has doubled every fifteen years. The result has been an increase in pollution and an increase in cost per person.

If the auto makers are successful in developing workable devices that will clean up the discharge of pollutants, this will add only about fifty dollars to the cost of an automobile—less than 2 percent of the average car's price. It is estimated that a lead-free antiknock gasoline can be developed which will raise the cost of the fuel only one cent per gallon. Removing the sulfur from fuel oil will cost only about one dollar per barrel.

The Department of Agriculture has estimated that air pollution is responsible for the loss each year of three

An example of the cost of air pollution in terms of loss of crops. The endive plant on the left was raised in nonfiltered air, and the one on the right was raised in filtered air

hundred twenty-five million dollars' worth of agricultural crops and one hundred seventy-five million dollars' worth of farm animals.

It costs the average citizen a great deal more to repair the damage caused by air pollution than it would cost to prevent it, even if the cost of prevention were passed on to him through higher taxes or increased prices for consumer goods. It probably costs the average individual about sixty-five dollars a year to repaint, repair, clean, wash, and replace possessions that have been damaged by pollutants. For a resident of New York City, the figure may be as high as two hundred dollars a year.

An interesting cost comparison was recently made in Clayton, Missouri, between the open burning of leaves by individuals and the collection of leaves by the city. The investigators found that it is much cheaper to collect the leaves than it is to let the citizens burn them in the streets.

To begin with, the homeowners of Clayton burned about five hundred tons of leaves per year, releasing about one hundred tons of hydrocarbons, nitrogen oxides, and fine particles into the air. This caused an average expense of about twenty cents per person per year in laundry and cleaning costs for residents and ten cents extra per year for the workers who commuted to the city. The total cost for laundry and cleaning came to five thousand dollars per year.

The extra costs for car washing were calculated at another five thousand dollars per year; and for property damage caused by pollutants, the additional expense was seventeen thousand dollars per year. No amount could be estimated for the medical bills arising from the allergies and other diseases resulting from the pollution. Fire loss was figured at two hundred fifty dollars per year, the damage to street paving by fire came to another two hundred fifty dollars, and the fire department cost for answering the alarms was still another two hundred and fifty dollars. Five hundred dollars' worth of trees and shrubbery were lost each year. The added cost of removing unburned leaves from sewer inlets was calculated at three thousand five hundred twenty-five dollars per year.

The personal cost to the citizens of Clayton who burned their own leaves thus came to eleven thousand two hundred fifty dollars, or twenty-two dollars and fifty

Burning leaves contribute greatly to air pollution

cents per ton of leaves, and the additional cost to the city itself came to about seven dollars per ton.

If the city picked up the leaves and burned them in pollution-controlled incinerators, the cost would be eight dollars and twenty cents per ton, a saving of more than twenty-one dollars per ton of leaves.

But enough of these dollars-and-cents figures. The problem is more than one of money. Additional medical bills may of course result from the effects of pollution on health, but how is it possible to put a price tag on the four hundred lives that were lost in the London fog of 1962? What is the real cost of the loss of health for countless thousands of people per year? What is it worth to eliminate the nagging coughs, watering eyes, and breathing difficulties from which many people suffer? How expensive is the loss of beauty, comfort, or happiness to those who must live in polluted areas?

Unfortunately, too many Americans do have to live, or at least work, in these polluted areas, since the greatest pollution occurs in the big cities. Late in 1967, the Public Health Service's National Center for Air Pollution Control announced that New York City was more heavily polluted than any of the other sixty-five most densely populated metropolitan areas of the United States. Following close behind were Chicago, Philadelphia, Los Angeles, Cleveland, Pittsburgh, Boston, Newark, Detroit, and St. Louis. The air over New York was more than five times more polluted than the air over High Point-Greensboro, North Carolina—the least polluted area of the sixty-five.

John T. Middleton, director of the Air Pollution Center, explained the causes of the polluted atmosphere in the top ten areas. To begin with, the first three—New York, Chicago, and Philadelphia—had the same type of problem, according to Middleton: large populations in small places, in which the power demands for improving living are met by local generation which burns high-sulfur fuels, and industry is located in mid-city.

Los Angeles is "a little unique; no industry, so no sulfur fuels. But a poor transportation system, so large quantities of gasoline are burned. Therefore smog. Los Angeles should be easier to cope with now that the federal government can control auto emissions."

Cleveland has "an archaic society which is not using the pollution-control techniques now available." Pittsburgh is "a changing problem. You must give them credit for their smoke-control program, but perhaps the city got a bit complacent."

He described Boston as "a low-level New York." In Newark, "industry has flourished. That says it all."

Detroit is "a typical industrial city, with transportation contributing to the problem. Control has been a subject for concern for fifteen years, but it is a flat plateau, with industry spread all over."

Finally, St. Louis has "an interstate problem. The city is surrounded by states with varying restrictions on pollution. It's also a thriving urban area, burning much sulfur fuel and gasoline."

As Thomas Williams of the Public Health Service Air Pollution Division points out, "Smog is a social disease —the product of people and their activities. And like other social diseases, if not dealt with, it only gets worse."

9

Our Defenses

Many years ago, in Pittsburgh, a group of business and financial leaders started the pollution control ball rolling by initiating plans to change the smoky image of the city. The construction of a huge petroleum complex in Dade County, Florida, was stopped when the Safe Progress Association, a group of twelve citizens, found that it would be a serious air polluter. Stamp Out Smog, an organization started by nine California women in 1958, has since enlisted the support of over four hundred business and civic organizations.

Such organizations as the League of Women Voters, the General Federation of Women's Clubs, the Junior Chamber of Commerce, and the National Association of Housing and Redevelopment Officials, to name but a few, have been very active in organizing citizens groups to investigate local air pollution problems. These local groups, clubs, and committees are our first line of defense against air pollution. State, local, and national legislation, as well as increased research, often results from the work of these people.

The second line of defense is local governmental control. Smoke coming from factories, homes, industry, and dumps should be cleaned up by regional agencies, because, as things stand now, the federal government looks upon this kind of stationary air pollution as a local problem. Of the many local agencies, probably the most notable and certainly the most active is the Los Angeles County Air Pollution Control District.

Other local governmental agencies are beginning to strengthen themselves. New York City's Department of Air Pollution Control, for example, has added new staff inspectors and new regulations. In 1966, soft coal for heating was outlawed and no new incinerators were licensed. Minimum standards were set for clean air. Plans were set up to begin automatic air pollution index reports, and it was proposed that the budget should be doubled— to three million dollars, or almost thirty-eight cents per person. This is still short of the fifty cents mentioned earlier, but it is a lot better than the former sixteen cents yearly per citizen.

One of the most unusual actions taken by the New York agency was in the field of research. For the first time in this country, in 1966, a municipal air pollution agency joined with a university to study pollution. The Cooper Union School of Engineering and the New York City De-

Almost no city is safe from smog attacks. It can happen in St. Louis (top); in San Francisco (center); it can even happen in the crystal-clear mountain air over Denver (bottom)

partment of Air Pollution Control formed the Department of Environmental Engineering at the college.

There have been other examples of local pollution control on a broader basis than city- or countywide. The governors of the states of New York, New Jersey, Delaware, and Pennsylvania have agreed to cooperate to beat the smoke and smog. State legislators from New York, New Jersey, and Connecticut offered identical control legislation to their legislatures.

The real problem in the area of air pollution-control legislation is that the aerial garbage does not respect state lines; it does not apply for a passport when it crosses any boundaries. One expert estimated that the air pollution from St. Louis—a city which has taken direct action to stop pollution—may drift as far as one hundred miles into the state of Illinois. The nasty part of this pollution drift is that the real polluter is not the one who suffers from the pollution.

Some people feel we are getting such a hodgepodge of local laws that we need federal control. This opinion is shared by some industrialists who find themselves financially hurt in their competition with other members of industry.

The third line of defense is federal legislation. The Federal Clean Air Act was set up in 1963, and it provided for research, training, and development in the field of scientific air pollution control. It also was set up to give funds to state, regional, and municipal air pollution-control agencies.

Under this law, and its 1965 amendments, the Secretary of Health, Education, and Welfare recommended a drastic reduction in the amount of pollution that can be given off by automobiles.

There is evidence that the federal government may get into the business of controlling stationary air pollution. After the President's Science Advisory Committee made its report on pollution in 1966, President Johnson urged in his State of the Union Message for 1967: "We should vastly expand the fight for clean air with a total attack on pollution at its sources, and because air, like water, does not respect man-made boundaries, we shall set up 'regional airsheds' throughout this great land."

A few months after this speech, the 1967 Air Quality Act was passed. Over a three-year period, Congress authorized the expenditure of three hundred and three million dollars for the continuing operation of air pollution-control facilities and one hundred and twenty-five million dollars for research in air pollution control.

As it stands now, the federal government can bring a state to court in order to make it obey federal controls. And, if one state causes pollution in another, fines can be imposed. The federal government can also include air pollution provisions in government contracts with industry in the same way that civil rights provisions are now included.

The federal government is getting so active that at one time there were at least five investigations going on at once. In each of these cases, one city or state was blaming another city or state for causing air pollution, and the federal government was trying to weigh the merits of the charges. New York was blaming New Jersey industry for air pollution by smoke. A Delaware town was blaming a Maryland rendering plant. A Vermont town was blaming a New York paper mill. Marietta, Ohio, was blaming a Parkersburg, West Virginia, steel mill. And Garrison, Montana, with a population then of ninety-three people, was accusing a Rocky Mountain phosphate plant of making invalids out of the citizens' cattle.

The federal government is also involved in the development of a fumeless bus. It has given one hundred fifty thousand dollars to the National Academy of Sciences to design and build this type of vehicle. It has been suggested that another ten million five hundred thousand dollars be set aside to encourage research, development, and demonstration of electric automobiles.

Taxes enter into the picture, too. Many people want tax exemptions for installing smoke-control devices in their factories. Others want higher taxes to be applied to the heavy polluters. Still others want taxes on automobiles to be raised as the cars get older and are more likely to become polluters.

In any case, our efforts must continue at an even faster pace. The technologists must keep ahead of public opinion.

Should the work of helping to eliminate air pollution be left up to adults? Definitely not. There are many things that young people can do, especially when they

are on school assembly committees, in scout groups, or
even when carrying out classroom assignments for school
projects. Here are some things you, as a student or private
individual, can do:

1. Become an informal pollution observer. Investigate the pollution situation in your town. Learn what the sources of air pollution are, what officials have the control responsibility in your area, and what is being done about the problem.

2. Arrange assembly programs or classroom talks by control and health officials, industry spokesmen, and representatives of groups working for clean air.

3. Write articles for your school newspaper to inform your fellow students about the fight to eliminate pollution.

4. Take field trips to controlled and uncontrolled air pollution sources.

5. Distribute circulars to your fellow townspeople. These circulars can be obtained from local, state, or national air pollution-control agencies.

6. Prepare air pollution-control posters and ask to have them displayed in local business and industrial establishments.

7. Schedule debates giving the pros and cons of such problems as whether control is best at the local or the national level of enforcement. Perhaps these debates could be broadcast by your local radio station.

10

Filth in the Sea

The visibility on the southwestern tip of England near Land's End was about eight miles on that day in March, 1967. It was broad daylight, and the merchant ship *Torrey Canyon* was steaming through the waves at about seventeen knots, bound for Wales from Kuwait with a cargo of crude oil.

The *Torrey Canyon* was soon to go down in history —in more ways than one. Because of a monumental mistake in navigation, this 61,263-ton vessel ran aground on Seven Stones Reef. Oil began pouring out of a tear in her side, six hundred and fifty feet long, forming slicks that threatened to foul the beautiful beaches of the Cornish coast.

Thirty-six ships were sent to the area to dump hundreds of tons of detergents into the sea in the hope of breaking up the oil slicks and sinking them before they could reach shore. Smaller boats did the same in the shallow water near shore. Two thousand British servicemen, along with firemen and civilians—men, women, and children—began to wash down the rocks along the coast.

But nothing could stop the oil. A beach would be cleared only to be fouled again by the next incoming tide. Naturalists warned that the detergents could have harmful effects on the oyster and mussel beds, as well as on the fish in the sea. Others said the oil slicks were shutting off the light and oxygen supply so necessary to underwater life. Birds, trapped in the oil, were dying at an alarming rate. More than one hundred thousand of them perished.

Suggestions were a dime a dozen. One person recommended filling the tanker with balloons and Ping Pong balls to refloat her. It was suggested that the oyster beds be covered with absorbent paper to protect them. Another person proposed using sonic booms from aircraft to coagulate the oil into globules that could be scooped up with fish nets.

An attempt was made to burn the oil off the beaches, but the result was a tarry mess. Foam rubber was strung across inlets to prevent the entry of the oil.

A Dutch tug tried to pull the *Torrey Canyon* free of the rocks, but it failed. At this point, more than thirty-five thousand tons of oil had escaped.

Ten days after going aground, the tanker split in two as a result of the terrific pounding of wind and waves. This meant that more oil began pouring into the sea. By this time, half of the ship's original cargo of one hundred and eighteen thousand tons had escaped. It became clear that the detergents could not do the job of ridding the coast of its horrible water pollution.

Something drastic had to be done. Although it was known that a serious air pollution situation could result,

Royal Air Force jets were sent in to bomb the tanker. The bombs set fire to the remaining crude oil in the ship's hull, and the fire spread across the surface of the ocean for more than a mile. Flames two hundred feet high shot into the air, and smoke rose to a height of one mile. Soot dropped as far away as the English Channel.

In order to keep the fire burning, more jets came in, dropping aviation fuel on the flames. Napalm bombs and rockets were also used. Still the oil flooded out of the seemingly unsinkable ship, and the blackening of the beaches continued.

In the meantime, polystyrene nets were being laid to prevent the oil from entering The Solent, a body of water separating the Isle of Wight from the mainland. The Royal Society for the Prevention of Cruelty to Animals sent in rescue teams to try to clean the oil from the birds trapped in the oily mess. Compressed air was shot through hoses at the site of the oyster beds in the hope that a water current could be created to force the oil off into another direction. Blankets of straw and chicken wire were spread over the oysters to prevent clogging by the oil scum at low tide.

By this time, the French oystermen were becoming concerned. The winds and the currents were bringing the oil toward the Normandy and Brittany coasts. Supplies of detergents were being stockpiled in the city of Brest.

Three weeks after the *Torrey Canyon* ran aground, the oil reached France, and ships were sent out to spray the oil slicks with chemicals. Fortunately, the scum was much thinner by the time it crossed the English Channel,

A water bird killed by oil pollution is not a pretty sight.
This one was destroyed by oily bilge water from a tanker.

and the French problem was not as acute as the British one had been. But the French fishermen had to move millions of young oysters by truck from the northern coast of Brittany, facing Britain, to the southern coast, facing the Atlantic Ocean. French birds also began to die.

What was the cost of the disaster? In addition to the millions of dollars lost in the sinking of the tanker, and the incalculable amount of money spent by the British and the French, there was the destruction of one hundred and twenty miles of beautiful English coastline. Thousands of birds, fish, plants, oysters, and mussels had been killed.

Once again man had proved his terrible ability to foul his natural surroundings. The story of the *Torrey Canyon* made headlines all over the world, but it is only one example of the ways in which our water is being constantly polluted.

11

Natural Waste and Hot Water

More than three hundred and fifty years ago, Captain John Smith and the settlers of the colony at Jamestown, Virginia, discovered so many fish in the clear, clean water of the Potomac River that they could almost be picked up by hand. Today, Arthur B. Hanson of the Coordinating Committee of the Potomac River valley, calls the river an "open cesspool" and "a natural sewage lagoon."

As recently as the 1920's, you could get a glass of pure water by turning on a tap almost anywhere in the United States. Today, this is not true. Smells, sediment, foam, and even typhoid, cholera, and dysentery micro-organisms may be found in the water you drink. We seem to be fast approaching the condition that was so well described by Coleridge in the *Rime of the Ancient Mariner:* "Water, water, everywhere,/Nor any drop to drink."

Where does the pollution come from? Basically, there are four different types of water pollution: natural, thermal, sewage, and industrial.

Natural pollution, as might be assumed, has always been with us. Since the first appearance of animals and

The open cesspool—pollution in the Potomac River

plants on the face of the earth, there has been waste material in water. Not only the natural body wastes of living things, but also dead organic matter often finds its way into our lakes, streams, rivers, and oceans.

Every time running water, including rain, flows over soil, rocks, and mineral deposits, there is a chance that organic wastes, sediment, and excess minerals may be added to the water supply. In the Southwest, parts of the Arkansas and the Red rivers are too salty for human consumption. A large-scale plan was carried out to cap some of the natural salt springs that contributed to this condition.

Clams in parts of Long Island Sound are dying because of natural body wastes from the ducks that are raised there. This may result in a loss of more than two and one-half million dollars to the clam raisers.

But man may also be guilty of contributing to natural pollution. When rain causes pesticides, fertilizers, and other chemicals to enter the water table from a farmer's land, man is responsible. All over the world, rivers have been polluted with these products, causing the death of millions of fish and billions of plants.

And, through thoughtless misuse of our forests, man has brought about an increase in natural pollution. When the land has been denuded of trees—those mighty absorbers of rainwater—the resulting amount of runoff water has been increased. This, in turn, causes more and more natural pollutants to enter rivers and lakes. If there is nothing more serious in it, the water is still contaminated with silt and dirt. And silt and dirt, even if they do not immediately poison living things in the water, at least make it a more difficult place for plants and animals to live. Green plants cannot get enough sunlight, and animals cannot seek out food because of reduced visibility.

Thermal pollution is usually found where power plants and factories contribute high-temperature materials to the water supply. It is the excess heat discharged into a stream, lake, or river, rather than the materials themselves, that causes the pollution.

Any increase in the natural temperature of a body of water upsets the natural balance in that water. Perhaps the fish cannot live in high temperatures. Perhaps the high temperature kills the natural food of the river life. Perhaps by accident a new plant is introduced that is better suited to the higher temperature. It may then crowd out the normal plant life of the area by using up too much of the oxygen in the water. In any event, hot water added in quantity to natural bodies of water creates a pollution problem.

Thermal pollution may also result whenever a road is built or a field is put into agricultural production, since these activities may cause a rise in the temperature of the nearby water. Often, as trees must be cut down, shade is removed, and the runoff water is warmer when it reaches the river.

Extra heat in the water does more than make living things uncomfortable. It may kill the animals in the water. It may cause animals to leave the area, in which case the result may be an overpopulation of the plant life that was formerly eaten by these animals.

One of the most serious effects of thermal pollution is a change in the physical properties of the water itself. Warm water cannot hold as much gas in solution as can cold water. This means that the oxygen content of the water will be reduced by heating. As an experiment, leave a glass of cold water in your kitchen overnight. The next morning, when the water will have warmed to room temperature, you will see bubbles on the inner surface of the glass. These bubbles are caused by the gas that precipitates out of solution as the water gets warmer.

Without oxygen, there is no life. The lower the oxygen content of the water, the fewer living things will be found in the water.

Of course, even where there is thermal pollution, the water is seldom so hot that no living things can exist in it. But it seems that our more desirable fish need more oxygen and a lower temperature than our less desirable ones do. Trout, salmon, and whitefish require very cold water. There have been cases in which a rise of two or three degrees in temperature has wiped out the trout population.

Sometimes the rise in temperature has been enough to eliminate even the warmer-water species, such as crappies, sunfish, and some types of bass. The result has been that the warmer water has become the home of carp, dogfish, and suckers.

12

Sewage Pollution

Sewage pollution is the type of pollution that the man in the street usually thinks of when he thinks of water pollution. It is often the most obvious to the naked eye or most odoriferous to the naked nose. This pollution consists of raw or partially treated domestic waste.

Sewage, of course, contains both liquid and solid wastes from human beings. It also contains anything else that goes down the drain into the house sewer. This means that bath water, sink and garbage disposal drainage, and water from washing machines will be found in this type of pollution.

Detergent foam also adds to sewage pollution. Slightly more than twenty years ago, the housewives in a small Pennsylvania town were given medium-sized samples of a new product—a detergent said to be far superior to soap for the washing of clothing and dishes. On the next Monday, the women of the town used their samples for the weekly wash.

The result was something like a huge snowstorm. Foam appeared in the sewage treatment plant and was scattered all over the area. It bubbled in the kitchen sinks and the shower baths. Thus began the detergent foam problem that was to extend across the length and breadth of the land.

About ten years later, in Suffolk County on New York's Long Island, most of the housing projects were affected by detergent foam. Almost one-third of the wells in the county contained this type of pollution. Half of the wells in the Minneapolis-St. Paul area suffered from this blight. By 1965, about 40 percent of the tested wells in thirteen states contained some detergent pollution.

Some apartment dwellers in New York City were amazed one day to find foam coming out of their taps

Detergent foam can be pretty, but it is a real pollution problem. Here it is in the fountain in front of the National Gallery of Art in Washington, D.C.

along with their drinking water. And the foam sometimes rose in the pipes as far as the seventh floor of the buildings.

In Chicago, a canal became so polluted with detergent foam that the water had to be sprayed with chemicals just to break up the bubbles.

The river at the Wisconsin Dells was covered with foam for some time. Chanute, Kansas, was inundated. Billows of foam rising to a height of fifteen feet were noted at the sewage treatment plant there.

Actually, any agent that promotes cleaning—even soap—can be called a detergent. But the products which have come to be referred to as detergents are chemical compounds—synthetic products sometimes called syndets (synthetic detergents)—that are used both in the

Detergent foam can cause a mess at the local sewage treatment plant. This one is in Altoona, Pennsylvania

home and in industry for cleaning purposes. The cause of the detergent mess was a chemical called ABS, once used in over 80 percent of the washing products. ABS is chemical shorthand for alkyl benzene sulfonate.

Only one part of an ABS type detergent in one million parts of water is enough to produce foam, and these kinds of detergents also resist up to 50 percent of the action of bacteria that break down sewage in treatment plants. The result is that most of the foam remains and therefore the pollution remains.

ABS detergents, in addition to being unpleasing to the eye when found in drinking water, can be health hazards, too. As little as sixteen parts per million in water can kill all of the mayfly larvae in a stream, and thus can destroy a lot of food for the fish. Ten parts per million can kill shrimp and crayfish. And Dr. R. D. Swisher of the Monsanto Company estimates that until 1964, the average level of detergent pollution in domestic sewage was about that much—ten parts per million.

ABS is now being replaced by less troublesome chemical compounds, but more about that later.

Detergent foam, being so visible, is the most obvious type of sewage pollution—but definitely not the most serious. As a matter of fact, it may have been a blessing in disguise, since it called the attention of millions of people to the problems of our ever-growing water pollution blight.

Far more serious is the increase in the epidemics among whole populations which are caused by sewage pollution of other kinds. Hepatitis is an example of a disease that has been on the rise among civilized people. For thousands of years this disease, often called jaundice, was quite common, especially in wartime, because of faulty or inadequate sewage treatment. Then it seemed to die out as sanitation practices became more efficient. But the viruses that cause this disease have developed some resistance to the chlorine which is used in the treatment of sewage.

Of course, not all cases of hepatitis can be traced to polluted water, but there is a great deal of evidence that water may be an important carrier of the disease. In one case, people who ate clams coming from polluted water in Long Island Sound came down with hepatitis. The same thing happened on the coast of New Jersey, and oyster eaters on the Gulf of Mexico also developed the disease. Physicians are beginning to recommend that clams be fried or steamed for at least five minutes in order to make them safe to eat.

In 1953 a polio epidemic broke out in Edmonton, Alberta, in Canada. Medical officials traced the disease to human waste in the North Saskatchewan River, from which the city gets its water.

It has been known for many years that typhoid fever is caused by microorganisms in human waste carried in the water. Yet Keene, New Hampshire, has had typhoid epidemics within recent memory, as have many other places. In 1965 some children found a watermelon floating in the Hudson River as it flowed past New York City. After they ate the melon, eight of the children came down with this disease.

In 1965, about eighteen thousand people in Riverside, California, were suddenly overcome by attacks of dysentery. The symptoms of this disease, caused in this case by unchlorinated water, are fever, nausea, cramps, and vomiting. Apparently, seepage of water from septic tanks and from storm runoff was to blame.

Just in terms of loss of recreation such as swimming and boating, or even loss of such necessities as drinking and cooking water, sewage pollution is a tremendous problem. At one time during the early 1960's the people of Rensselaer, New York, were forced to boil their drinking water because the Hudson River was so polluted.

The Hudson River is one of the most polluted rivers in the United States. An adventurous man was living on a reconditioned Chinese junk at one of the docks in New York City. When the man was interviewed on his boat by a local television newsman, he was asked: "Aren't you afraid to live here by yourself? What if you fell overboard in the middle of the night? What would you do then?"

His answer was simple. "The first thing that I'd do is to take massive typhoid shots."

The late Senator Robert Kennedy of New York, when looking at the Hudson River, was quoted as saying, "If you fall in here, you don't drown—you decay."

In the last thirty years, the giant sea sturgeon of the Hudson has almost completely disappeared because of the pollution. And at one time these fish were so plentiful that their eggs (caviar) were even shipped to Russia, usually thought of as the main source of caviar. The oysters in the Hudson have all but died out, as have the clams and many smaller animals that serve as food for the fish. The only good news coming out of the Hudson River pollution story is that the teredo, a shipworm that bores into wooden pilings, is also losing its fight for life.

One of the chief effects of the dumping of raw waste into water is the removal of oxygen from the water. This, of course, cuts down on the number of organisms that can live there. Now let's illustrate with a little arithmetic. The waste from one human being, when dumped into the Hudson River, removes the equivalent of seventeen-one hundredths of a pound of oxygen from the water. Multiply this by the one million, two hundred forty-two thousand people whose waste is ejected into the river between Albany and New York City and we come up with the amazing figure of over two hundred thousand pounds— more than one hundred tons—of oxygen being removed from the water of this river every day.

Then there are other little problems along the Hudson. For example, when tugboat men went out on strike during 1967, there was no one to tow the sewage and garbage scows out to sea, and the raw pollution had to be dumped over the side. In addition, new, stricter rules against the use of garbage incinerators in New York City have resulted in the dumping of garbage into the river, since it cannot be burned because of these laws. This is a case of causing water pollution in an attempt to control air pollution.

Chesapeake Bay is also contaminated. At the turn of this century, the bay produced as many as twelve million bushels of oysters per year. Today, because of pollution, the yield is closer to one million bushels, and it is becoming smaller and smaller every year. No longer can seafood restaurants advertise that "The oyster and crab you eat today/Slept last night in Chesapeake Bay."

Consider the mighty Mississippi River. Mark Twain would never recognize it. In some places, any modern-day Huckleberry Finn who floated down the river on a raft would be taking his life in his hands. This magnificent river has become the sewer for hundreds of cities and thousands of industries, and it is called by some pollution

These warning signs on Lake Michigan beaches at Hammond, Indiana, have become almost permanent

Two technicians compare samples of Mississippi River water. The clear jug holds a sample from the river's headwaters near Itasca Park, Minnesota. The other jug contains a sample from the river's mouth at New Orleans

experts "the colon of America." Until 1962, the city of St. Louis alone was pumping two hundred thousand gallons of liquid human waste and four hundred tons of solid human waste into the river daily. St. Louis has stopped most of this, but to do it cost the city almost one hundred million dollars.

Lake Michigan is in trouble, too. In 1964 the beaches on the South Side of Chicago were closed for two months because of pollution, and the beaches of Hammond, Indiana, have been closed since the early 1950's—so long that most people cannot even remember when these beaches were safe for swimming.

Pollution in Lake Michigan, especially pollution by dead plant bodies, was so thick in 1965 that it often

blocked the intake pipes of the water company. Hyman
G. Gerstein, Chicago's chief water engineer at the time,
reported that the southern end of the lake was so badly
polluted he feared that chemical treatment could no
longer make the water fit to drink. In 1965, also, the
United States Public Health Service made a study that
pointed out the problems. Much has to be done in order
to correct the situation.

Even the island paradises are having their problems
with water pollution. Puerto Rico and the Virgin Islands
have long dumped raw sewage into their streams and off-
shore waters. Unless reforms are made immediately, the
Public Health Service recently warned, there is danger of
a great health menace and a resulting decrease in the
tourist trade on these islands.

The United States is not the only country suffering
from sewage pollution. On the Danube River above Brati-
slava, Czechoslovakia, the pollution reading is about
forty times greater than the safe amount. Vienna, Austria,
has no sewage treatment plant and uses this river. In fact,
to quote a Czech scientist, Dr. Adolph Hermann, "The
Danube is rapidly becoming the main European sewage
channel."

From the time man first appeared on this planet until he began living in towns and cities, he could depend
upon his water supply to clean itself. Worms and snails
in the rivers ate the solid pollutants that sank to the bottom. Certain kinds of bacteria in the water would dispose
of the dissolved pollutants and some of the material that

was suspended. While carrying on photosynthesis, one-celled plants, called algae, would furnish oxygen to the water.

But man began to pollute his water more and more. And soon the natural purifying organisms in the water—in rivers, lakes, and streams—were not numerous enough to clean the water. Something had to be done, and the answer seemed to be the construction of sewers, sewage treatment plants, and septic tanks.

Today, most cities and towns in the United States have sewage treatment plants. This is not true all over the world, however. Vienna has already been mentioned as a large city without such a plant, and until 1967 the entire province of Quebec, in Canada, had none. This is the province in which Quebec City and Montreal are located, and the very first sewage disposal plant in the territory was built there to handle the refuse at "Expo 67."

Most plants use a method known as *Primary Sewage Treatment*. This is strictly a physical, rather than a chemical, process. The main treatment is one of settling. Although there may be screens on the input pipes to trap the larger pieces of pollution, the water is merely pumped into settling tanks where the solids settle to the bottom. Primary treatment removes 35 percent of the solid material from raw sewage.

Many treatment plants then take this water and use a process called *Secondary Sewage Treatment*. This almost always involves the use of bacteria, so it might be called a biological method of purification. Certain kinds of bacteria are added to the water, and these microorganisms use the pollutants for food. This is what usually happens, not only in sewage treatment plants, but also in septic tanks. When the sewage is decomposed, the bacteria are often removed by another settling process.

What remains may be water that is safe to drink, but most cities add chemicals to the water to kill disease bacteria and viruses or to cut down on harmless, though unpleasant, odors. The water is often aerated and filtered, also.

There are other methods of removing pollution from the water, but these stages of treatment are the most common. If they are so efficient, however, why are we bothered by pollution from our homes and sewers?

Primary sewage treatment (left): The sewage enters the grit chamber where solid materials settle out. The large pieces of sewage are prevented from entering the plant by the bar screen. Smaller pieces enter the comminutor and are ground to sizes that can be handled by the treatment plant. But primary sewage treatment may not be enough. The water may still be contaminated (right)

The first answer is that adequate sewage treatment is fantastically expensive. The total investment in sewage treatment plants in the United States alone is counted in billions of dollars—about twelve billion dollars, to be more exact.

The second answer is that our sewer systems have not caught up with the population of this country. In 1942 the sewage from almost thirty million people was dumped in a raw state into rivers and streams; the sewage from about twenty-five million people received some sort of primary treatment; and the sewage of twenty-one million people was given secondary treatment. This left over sixty million people with no sewers at all, although many of them had septic tanks.

In 1962 the raw sewage of only about fifteen million people was dumped into the water, and primary treatment was available for the sewage of about forty-two million people. Secondary treatment of sewage leaped to include more than sixty million people, which was a big jump. But the population had grown so much that more than sixty-eight million persons in this country were then without sewers.

The third answer is evident only after a heavy rain. Dr. Luther L. Terry, when he was Surgeon General of the United States, pointed out that we will be in serious trouble if we cannot keep our sewage water and our rainwater separate. In 1965, there were thirteen hundred cities with a combined population of about twenty-six million people that had combined storm and sewage pipes leading into their sewage treatment plants. During a rainstorm, therefore, the treatment plant was terribly over-loaded, and the result was an overflow of untreated sewage into a river, stream, or lake. Furthermore, if rain-water is diluted with sewage water, even on sunny days, all of the water reaching the treatment plant will be uni-formly polluted.

If separate sewer lines were built, the cost of the sewage treatment could be reduced a great deal, but building these installations can cost a lot of money. One such project is being carried out in Washington, D.C., and will probably cost the city more than one billion dol-lars. It has been estimated that the separation of storm and sanitary sewers in the other large cities in the United States will cost more than forty billion dollars.

13

Industrial Pollution

"Lake Erie Is Dying . . . Does Anybody Care?" asked the advertisements in Cleveland newspapers. Billboards read "Stop Killing Lake Erie . . . Fight Pollution." In this way began a campaign to rescue one of our largest bodies of water from the dread disease of pollution.

The campaign was started by one man—David L. Blaushild, an automobile dealer from Shaker Heights, Ohio. As a boy, he had played near Shaker Lakes—once a beautiful series of ponds near Lake Erie. But a few years ago, when he was taking his small daughter to see this area, he discovered that the ponds were now a series of sewage-filled, lifeless bodies of liquid garbage. When he investigated further, he found that almost all of the creeks and rivers emptying into Lake Erie near Cleveland were being destroyed by pollution. Even the lake itself had developed areas where fish could not live; beaches had been closed because of the pollution; and the public seemed not to care. It was at this point that Blaushild began to finance the advertising in newspapers and on billboards—out of his own pocket.

Pollution flowing out of Cleveland Harbor into Lake Erie (above), and a closeup of the contamination along Cleveland's lakefront (below)

Soon people began to write letters to public officials, urging the enforcement of pollution laws and the building of new sewage treatment plants. Blaushild found that he had friends. And, after two hundred thousand people had expressed concern, *The Cleveland Press,* in 1963, began its own campaign. Ohio's governor, James A. Rhodes, called for a pollution-control conference, and many city and industrial polluters were forced to begin planning better water treatment plants.

But the battle has not been won. After all, parts of the states of Michigan, Ohio, Pennsylvania, New York, and the province of Ontario, Canada, have contributed to the horrible pollution of Lake Erie. The United States Public Health Service has said that this lake is deteriorating at a frightening rate. It is the shallowest of the Great Lakes, and along its edge is an industrial belt that stretches for three hundred miles, from Detroit to Buffalo. There are also more than ten million people living near its shores. That can mean a lot of pollution. If more is not done soon, the lake may be killed.

Everyone seems to know a story about water pollution from industrial waste. A boy wades into a stream polluted by dyes coming from a wallpaper factory, and the skin on his legs and feet begins to peel off. The local river begins to smell revolting during hot weather. Animal parts dumped into the river by a packinghouse cause gas bubbles to rise to the surface of the water. Even landfill projects carried on by industry send silt into the water.

There is little need to list all of the countless varieties

of garbage that industries commonly throw into the water. But we do need to consider the horrible effects of the common types of pollution—literally, the run-of-the-mill kinds of waste. Water is made unfit for human use. Many new obnoxious plants can grow. Smells emerge. And fish and other water creatures are killed.

Waste pollution from industries and factories is a many-faceted thing. It is the broadest category of all, and there are at least as many types of industrial wastes as there are different types of industry. But this kind of pollution can be subdivided into six broad areas.

Floating Matter. Here we find froth, oil, and floating

The sad ending of a fish kill in the Connecticut River

solids. Froth can be the result of cleaning with detergents, and it also can come from certain mineral flotation processes. These processes are used to separate minerals from their ores. The ore is pulverized, mixed with oil and water, and whipped into a foam. In this way, the mineral mixes with the oil, floats, and can be skimmed off the top of the mixture, but much of the foam remains.

Oil drains into the water from certain chemical processes, from oil refineries, from any factory where machinery is carelessly lubricated, and from metalworking shops where the metal is bathed in oil. Oil in fresh and salt water also can come from disasters such as the *Torrey Canyon* episode, as well as from careless tanker crews who might pump overboard ballast water fouled with oil.

Floating solids, such as bark or sawdust, come from pulp mills and paper manufacturers. Fibers from clothing mills also float. Food pulps from canning factories and coke particles from coke plants are found in water.

Waste water containing floating matter is treated by first sending the water into a mixing and equalizing tank. Here the water is made uniformly polluted, since it is easier to treat when it is homogenous. The mess is then sent into a flotation unit, where air bubbles are used to help float the solids so that they can be removed. Two types of chemicals are added: one to cause the smaller particles to lump together into larger ones; and one to break up the oily particles. Antifoams and coagulants may also be added, and the treated water, although it is still far from being pure, can then be pumped away—minus the floating matter it once contained.

Settleable Solids. These pollutants from industry are also relatively large particles, as were the floating solids, except that these sink instead of float. Metal filings and turnings from metal shops and factories are commonly found in water. Anything that falls from the air and then sinks comes under this category, such as flue dust from steel mills and silt from smokestacks.

Runoff from storm waters can contribute to pollution, too, even to the extent of carrying large tin cans into the stream. Coal dust, cement, mineral particles, and all other materials lost in manufacturing processes are common pollutants.

With the settleable solids, the problem is to get them to sink faster than they usually do. To accomplish this, coagulants are added to the water to cause the smaller particles to group together and settle faster. The water is then filtered and dumped.

Colloidal Matter. A colloid is a special type of mixture consisting of small particles suspended in a fluid medium. A colloid is different from a solution in that the suspended particles are greater than molecular in size. For example, starch in water is a colloid, as are small particles of smoke suspended in air. In a colloidal suspension, the particles will not settle out in a short period of time, and this makes them difficult to remove.

In industry, colloids can be caused when materials such as polishing compounds are put in water. Some minerals will form them, too. Other particles in this category are some types of oils used in metalworking.

Colloidal wastes also can come from human sewage,

food processing chemicals, and some solvents and other chemical industry products and by-products. Waste liquids from the food industry, pulp-and-paper-mill additives, textile sizing materials, and certain dyes used in paper, food, and clothing material can form this type of pollution.

There are several ways to remove the colloidal matter from industrial waste water, but two processes are the most common. A sedimentation unit can be used, and the process is almost the same as the one that removes settleable solids, or a dialyzer can be used. In this unit, the raw sewage and water are pumped into a chamber that contains a membrane with very small pores. These pores are small enough to keep out most of the waste matter but large enough to let through certain salts. The salts are then reclaimed, and the polluted water is pumped into another chamber in which microbes are present that can begin digesting the waste in the water.

Dissolved Solids. One common dissolved solid is the mineral salt. These salts can be chemical by-products or they may be natural minerals that have been coagulated after going through an industrial process. Organic matter may also dissolve when it goes through a rinsing process. There are also other types of dissolved solids, such as degreasers, wood pulp cooking liquids, and waste from the cleaning of boilers. Wastes of this kind can occur in pickling processes, cleaning fluids, and plating and etching fluids.

Dissolved solids can be removed from waste water by a process very similar to that used in a common home water softener. Most of the dissolved solids are charged electrically, so all that is needed is a substance that will attract the solid particles and hold them. Remove the substance from the water, and you are also removing all of the dissolved solid particles that cling to it.

Toxic Substances. These are the pollutants that poison living things or change the environment in such a way as to cause the death of plants and animals. Plating and steel mills may contribute cyanide poisons to the water; coke and chemical plants may produce phenols, such as carbolic acid.

There are other kinds of relatively uncommon industrial pollutants—those that cause cancer. At least three chemical elements are carcinogenic. These are arsenic, beryllium, and chromium. Arsenic is the most common pollutant of the three. Add to this the radioactive elements and certain hydrocarbons sometimes found in our waters, and a very real cancer threat arises out of water pollution.

Arsenic can be found in waste waters from certain mines, and the carcinogenic hydrocarbons may reach the water after distillation operations and after the burning of coal and oil. Fish with cancer of the mouth have been found near oil refineries. Even our old enemy, benzopyrene, has been found in barnacles and oysters in water contaminated by oil. And oil itself is a common pollutant, not only off the coast of Wales, but also in many other places from Maine to California.

Dieldrin, DDT, chlordane, and other pesticides are suspected of being carcinogens, also. While it is true that we are far more likely to get these substances into our systems from eating vegetables than we are from drinking water that is polluted, it is still best for us to keep them out of our rivers.

Pesticides, such as the chemicals used to kill insects, and herbicides, such as crabgrass killers, are always a pollution hazard near the factories where they are manufactured. Heavy metal salts, such as lead acetate, can be poisonous, too.

Radioactive waste may also be present in the water. Just a few years ago, it was discovered that the Animas River in Colorado was becoming radioactive. At certain points, the water was from 40 to 160 percent more radioactive than the maximum safety level. It turned out that this condition was caused by a uranium processing plant in Durango, Colorado. Farther down the river, the radioactive water was being used on crops, and still farther down, it was being used as drinking water.

Even if industry is careful to dump so few radioactive materials into the water that the water remains safe for human consumption, trouble can arise. At one time the scientists at the Oak Ridge (Tennessee) National Laboratory were trying a method of waste disposal by which they poured radioactive materials into the river. Of course they did this with only the most harmless waste, and they kept a close check on their disposal methods. For example, strontium 90, ruthenium 106, and cobalt 60 had made the water radioactive, but when they measured the radioactivity level of the water, it was always low—safe for humans.

After doing this for some time, they began to measure the radioactivity level of the sediment in the water, too. Here came the first shock. The cesium 137, also dumped with the other waste, had become attached to the sediment of the river, rather than to the water. This meant that the radioactivity would not be diluted nearly as fast as if it had been in the water only.

Then came the second shock. Freshwater clams as far away as one hundred and fifty miles from the laboratory had collected strontium 90 in their bodies. They did not get rid of it, but kept on building it up. Some of the clams gave a reading of up to ten thousand times more radioactivity than the surrounding water. Needless to say, this method of disposal was abandoned by the laboratory.

There are many types of pollutants that consume the oxygen in the water, making it impossible for most plants

Waste water is not always treated by industry. This is pollution caused by a pulp-and-paper mill

and animals to live there. Organic matter from food manufacturing plants, pulp-and-paper mills, and chemical and textile factories may do this. Oil refineries, smelters, and chemical plants may discharge certain types of poisonous sulfides into the water.

Toxic substances, except for radioactive materials, are removed most often by bacterial action. Of course chemicals are used, too, in some cases, to speed up the action of the bacteria or to kill undesirable microorganisms. Then the water is filtered and ejected into a lake or stream.

Sludge. This final type of industrial pollutant is a concentration of solids thick enough to give the water a pastelike appearance. Some types of sludge come from sewage treatment plants and from food processors, refineries, chemical plants, and pulp-and-paper mills. The sludge from these sources is often organic. Since it contains carbon, most of it can be burned. Inorganic sludge can come from water softeners, from chemical plants, and from paint manufacturers. It also may be formed from sand and silt.

Sludge is eliminated in two steps. In the first step, the solids are removed from the fluid through the use of a vacuum filter. A vacuum filter, in this case, is a drum covered with cloth, with a vacuum inside. This is inserted into the watery waste and rotated. Naturally, the solid parts of the sludge tend to stick to the cloth when they are brought into contact with it by the force of the vacuum. Then the filter is removed, and the solids are scraped off the cloth. The solids can then be burned.

Some industries are discovering ways to make water treatment almost pay for itself. For example, in East Chicago, Indiana, at a steel mill, mill scale is being recovered from waste water. Mill scale is a type of iron compound that forms on steel when it is heated, and it was formerly washed away in waste water. Since the iron content of the scale can run as high as 70 percent, by recovering it, the steel mill is saving an average of eleven dollars per ton, or the considerable sum of almost two thousand dollars a day.

Oil refineries in the United States, it is estimated, are recovering as much as forty million dollars' worth of sulfur from waste water. Some industries convert their refuse in fertilizer plants and then sell the product for use on crops and lawns.

But if we are to continue the fight against water pollution, we must have better treatment systems. Scientists and technicians are busy helping us to catch up with increasing needs.

14

Water in Our Future

The really disturbing part of the water pollution story is that our supplies of water—polluted and non-polluted —are so very limited. Although there are about three hundred and twenty-six million cubic miles of water on the earth, Dr. Raymond L. Nace of the United States Geological Survey estimates that 99 percent of this total is salt water or ice; and, therefore, not usable for human needs.

Also, we cannot use more than one-third of the water that falls from the sky. The other two-thirds either evaporates back into the air, is used by plants, or becomes runoff into the sea or under the ground. Approximately thirty inches of water fall on the United States every year, but only about nine inches of it become usable groundwater, lake water, river water, and stream water.

Indeed, some of the places where man used to obtain fresh, clean water are disappearing. Along the coastline of the United States, such as in Los Angeles and on Long Island, humans have so drained their natural supply of water that sea water is seeping into the water table and replacing the clear water that is used up. Even Hawaii is leaking. Fresh groundwater on these islands is escaping into the ocean from two hundred and nineteen places along the shore. More than one hundred million gallons per day are being lost into Hilo Bay alone.

This loss of good water cannot continue. More and more people are demanding more and more clean water every year. It has been estimated that the modern city family uses six times more water today than yesterday's farm family did when wells were the main source of water. It may take three gallons of water to flush a toilet. Thirty gallons of water may flow into a bathtub just to clean one person. More than that may be used to wash a load of clothing. Some large air-conditioning units use enough water in cooling a restaurant to meet the daily needs of more than thirty thousand people.

Industry also uses tremendous quantities of water. As factories begin to use more and more complicated processes to turn out newer and newer products, their need for water skyrockets. Today, about half of the water used in the United States is used by industrial plants.

It takes about fifty thousand gallons of water to produce one ton of paper. A ton of copper requires one hundred thousand gallons. One ton of rayon uses up two hundred thousand gallons. A ton of aluminum needs three hundred and twenty thousand gallons, and a ton of synthetic rubber takes six hundred thousand gallons. A large steel mill may use enough water to supply one day's needs for all the people in Cleveland or Detroit.

Farmers, too, are using more water than ever before for irrigation. One ton of barley requires three hundred and fifty thousand gallons of water. A ton of corn needs four hundred thousand gallons, and wheat will use four hundred and fifty thousand gallons per ton.

Where will we get the water that our rising population requires just to stay alive? According to Dr. Charles C. Bradley of Montana State College, every person on the face of the earth needs at least two quarts of water per day—just to replace the water he loses from his body every twenty-four hours. Of course this does not mean that a human must drink all of this water. It may come from other beverages, or vegetables, or meat. But he must have his two quarts. Obviously, he must eat, too. And eating increases his water needs in still another way.

Let's apply a little arithmetic. Suppose we went on a bread-and-water diet—unpleasant as that may be. This would increase our water consumption per person per day to more than three hundred gallons, because of the amount of water necessary to raise enough wheat to make the two and one-half loaves of bread that we would need in order to stay alive.

But suppose we want a little more variety in our diet. Say we want some meat and vegetables. With the addition of one pound of meat and enough interesting vegetables per day to whet our appetites, our daily water requirement soars to two thousand five hundred gallons per day. The meat-producing animal has eaten vegetables that have used up water, and it has been drinking water itself. For every pound of meat obtained from the animal, we have invested two thousand three hundred gallons of water per day. The vegetables that we threw into our diets account for another two hundred gallons per day.

So, on a bread-and-water diet we would be using one hundred thousand gallons of water per person per year. And if we want better food, we require nearly one million gallons per person every year.

Dr. Bradley took these figures and did a little more arithmetic of his own. He calculated the amount of water available to the people of the United States every year. The final figure he arrived at was the number of people our supply of water can support—two hundred and thirty million persons. The frightening thing about this is that the United States Department of Health, Education, and Welfare expects the population of the United States to reach this figure by the late 1970's.

Dr. Bradley was not, by the way, including the vast amounts of water necessary to make fibers, to process lumber and paper products, to make steel, to run air-conditioners, to wash clothes, to take baths, and to perform countless other services.

What can we do about it? The only answer is that we must learn to reuse water on a scale much more lavish than we are doing at present, and our main obstacle in doing this is the problem of water pollution. We must prepare ourselves to produce drinkable water in huge quantities. The late 1970's are not far off. Indeed, they may be upon us before we are prepared.

15

On the Science Front

One of the most ambitious scientific programs in history was begun in 1965 to learn more about the water of the world. The ten-year-long study, called the International Hydrological Decade, was undertaken by one hundred and one countries, and scientists are participating all over the world.

One of the main projects to be undertaken during this decade is to find out just where the water of the world is at any given time. How much of it is in the air? How much of it is in bodies of water or under the ground? How much of it is in living things? And what is man doing to change the availability of the world's water?

Part of the work of the scientific group from the United States is to set up monitoring stations at fifty-one points throughout the country. Technicians at these stations will observe river discharges. In addition, there will be stations to monitor twelve different river basins.

New techniques are being used to record data. Radar measures rain- and snowfall. Moisture is measured with atomic detectors in deep holes in the earth. Even satellite monitoring is used. By 1975 we should be well on our way toward understanding facts about the water cycle and water pollution we are not even aware of at this time.

In the meantime, research is going on in other areas. Dr. J. F. Anderson, a biologist at the Connecticut Agricultural Experiment Station in New Haven, has found a new antibiotic pesticide. The product is a relative of penicillin, and it seems to destroy certain insect pests very efficiently. The best part of the story is that, even if it gets into our drinking water, it does not seem to be harmful to either man or his domestic animals.

Several universities have hydrological laboratories, although, of course, the work being done is on a smaller scale than that of the International Hydrological Decade laboratories. For example, the Potamological (related to the biological study of flowing water) Institute at the University of Louisville is doing a great deal of monitoring of the Ohio River. Technicians there are recording the amounts of pollutants—chemicals, microorganisms, algae, and other waste materials—in a seventy-three-mile stretch of the river. They also record the volume of flow, the speed, depth, temperature, and currents of the water, as well as light penetration into the lower depths of the river.

A wallet-sized water tester has been developed by Westinghouse Laboratories, primarily for use by servicemen in the field. It consists of a tough plastic card in which chemicals are sealed. The plastic cover is peeled off, and the card is placed into the water being tested. If the water is contaminated, a color change will occur. This simple device replaces a complete laboratory kit containing a flask, six chemicals, and assorted glassware. It should be ideal as a help in tracing pollution back to its source.

The war on typhus and hepatitis may be drawing to a close, if a new water treatment process can be used practically. Three chemists of the Monsanto Company found that the viruses causing these diseases can be removed from water by using a filter made from an organic compound—maleic anhydride—often used to coat paper.

Scientists at work. Water samples from polluted water will be taken back to the laboratory for analysis

Dr. K. L. Schulze, of Michigan State University, knew that the water at the East Lansing sewage treatment plant was being dumped into the Red Cedar River after secondary treatment. Even so, only 35 percent of the pollutants had been removed. He decided to try an unusual method of tertiary, or third stage, treatment in his laboratory. Water from the treatment plant was sent through a tank containing microscopic plants and animals and certain kinds of worms. He also installed screens, thermometers, lights, and air diffusers in his aquarium.

The living things removed from 85 to 95 percent of the pollution from the water. The resulting water was so pure that Dr. Schulze was able to raise guppies and water plants in it. He points out that the water, although some plants and animals can live in it, still contains chemicals such as phosphates, nitrates, and potassium, but it would be ideal for agricultural irrigation.

Experiments are being conducted in Europe, too. Studies are being made of the Trent River in England. This river is an essentially clean river to begin with, but as it passes the city of Stoke-on-Trent, it becomes polluted. Then, in the next fifty miles, water in the Trent recovers enough purity to support fish life. But it becomes polluted again when the Tame River joins it, bringing sewage and industrial waste down from Birmingham. For the next eight miles, the Trent again is unable to support fish life.

Several plans are being developed to keep the Trent clean. An artificial lake may be created to catch polluted water and hold it for about five days, after which it will be dumped back into the river. This would give the water enough time to absorb needed oxygen and enough time for sludge to settle out. Other plans are being considered to increase the flow rate of the river and thus hasten purification. Some people have advised a system of sludge settling tanks combined with aerators.

One of the most important scientific triumphs over water pollution was the development of detergents that would not be so difficult to eliminate.

As we indicated earlier, the first detergents contained alkyl benzene sulfonate—ABS—that was broken down by bacteria only very slowly and produced excessive foam. A search was started for a chemical that would be as effective in a detergent but which would be more biodegradable—more capable of being degraded or broken down by biological methods. The slang terms "hard detergent," for less biodegradable, and "soft detergent," for more biodegradable materials, were given to the products.

Early in the search, British scientists came up with a chemical that would make a fine soft detergent, but it was rather expensive. Then chemists in the United States discovered two more new compounds. They found that either SAS (sodium alkane sulfonate) or LAS (linear alkylate sulfonate) could be substituted for ABS, and the result was a soft detergent. Detergent manufacturers switched to the new chemicals, at a cost of about one hundred and fifty million dollars.

Eutrophication—an aging process—is being studied

by scientists. This process can be defined as the rate at which plant nutrients, usually nitrogen and phosphorus, enter a body of water. Excessive eutrophication is creating a problem in Lake Erie, and all over the world as well. As waste enters the water and enriches a lake so that algae can grow more rapidly, trouble arises: the lake can be choked with weeds that will grow in the fertile water; plant material may clog water intakes to the waterworks; drinking water may taste terrible; and it also may cause types of intestinal upsets. As a lake dies, it becomes less and less usable by man.

Eutrophication in action. Algae in this Virginia farm pond indicate that the water is too nutritious

Research scientists are trying to find a way to cut down the plant nutrition that flows into our waters. Dr. Robert Safferman of the Federal Water Pollution Control Administration has discovered a virus that eliminates some of the algal growth in the water. Plans have been suggested for running treated sewage through a series of ponds before it is dumped into a large body of water. These ponds would contain plant life that would remove many of the nutrients from the water before it reached the lake. Chemicals are being sought that would combine with the nutrients to form other compounds which could be removed easily from the water.

Pennsylvania State University is working on the problem of reducing nutrient flow into rivers and lakes. In an experiment going on at the university, water rich in nutrient waste is used to irrigate fields. As the water seeps down through the soil, the nutrients fertilize crops. Then the water, by now almost pure, flows into the ground-water supply under the soil. Not only are the crops more healthy and productive, but pure water is also returned to the earth to be used later by man when drawn from wells.

Industrial pollution, a more complicated problem than the pollution from home sewage, is being attacked on a grand scale by the scientists and technicians employed by industry. For example, a strainer that covers an area twenty feet by forty feet has been built at a cost of three hundred thousand dollars. For years, charcoal has been used as a filtering element in such things as ciga-

Pulp waste floating down the Pigeon River in North Carolina. The paper mill in the background is contributing to air pollution as well

rettes and whiskey stills. Charcoal, made from pulverized coal, is used in this new filter also, and it can treat about one and one-half million gallons of waste water daily.

A new installation has been set up at a Pennsylvania pulp-and-paper mill. At this mill, three main kinds of wastes were being dumped into the water: pulp and noxious liquids from the pulp mill, chemicals from the paper-making machines, and ashes from the power plant.

Now the waste water is screened to remove the large particles. Then it goes to a settling tank and a sludge trough. Next it goes to a lagoon where floating material is removed and bacteria—harmless to man—can act upon any remaining waste.

In a glass-fiber manufacturing plant, the problem waste was starch and rejected glass fibers. The water was first acted upon by bacteria to remove the starch and then screened to remove the glass fibers. A food processing plant, which gives off waste water from the washing of vegetables, uses this water to irrigate the factory lawns.

Oil pollution is becoming a complex problem—not only in situations such as the one caused by the *Torrey Canyon* but also from the everyday operations of industry and shipping. The British government is putting radioactive tracer atoms in oil waste so that as the waste travels its movements can be followed with Geiger counters.

Much more research on waste disposal is essential. Perhaps we can discover a medium other than fresh water for transporting our wastes. Some persons recommend the development of containers for pollutants or the use of flowing saltwater systems. Viruses may someday be found that will do a much better secondary purification job than bacteria. Tertiary water treatment is a wide-open field about which not much is known.

Chemists must find ways to degrade such compounds as DDT in our waste waters. Plastics are a waste problem,

This mine waste has been treated with chemicals

too; and we have no efficient way to dispose of them before they reach a stream or river. Large-scale desalting methods that are not too expensive must be developed. At the present time we do not know how to dispose effectively of the salts and acids that drain from mines. Finally, we know practically nothing about how to cleanse the oceans. They are becoming more and more polluted, and they are so large that we have no way of coping with them.

16

Paying for Pure Water

In 1965 we dumped four billion pounds of raw sewage into the waterways of the United States. We cannot afford to do that much longer, or we will be unable to get a drink of fresh water. Dr. Athelstan Spilhaus of the University of Minnesota Institute of Technology has said: "We don't *consume* anything. We simply convert every product we touch into waste."

It may cost ten billion dollars to clean up Lake Erie, and even then there is no assurance that the job can be done. In recent years, St. Louis spent ninety-five million dollars, Chicago spent one hundred and five million dollars, and Cincinnati spent sixty-six million dollars—all for new sewage treatment plants.

Abel Wolman, emeritus professor of sanitary engineering at Johns Hopkins University, reports that the people of the United States will have to invest more than eight hundred million dollars per year for the next ten years just to replace outmoded sewage treatment plants, add needed ones, and, in general, to catch up with the population explosion. But, he adds, to extend sewage

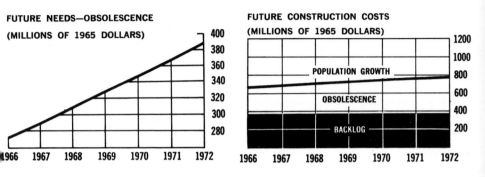

FUTURE NEEDS—OBSOLESCENCE
(MILLIONS OF 1965 DOLLARS)

FUTURE CONSTRUCTION COSTS
(MILLIONS OF 1965 DOLLARS)

POPULATION GROWTH

OBSOLESCENCE

BACKLOG

This is what we need, and what it will cost

treatment to those who do not now have it may require an additional eight hundred million dollars per year.

This money must be spent, and ultimately the cost must be borne by the public. Whether the funds come from federal taxes, or from industry—in which case the result would be higher prices for consumer goods—the people must pay. However, it may not cost us as much as we might think. Secretary of the Interior Stewart L. Udall has pointed out: "The tragic condition of many of the waters of this country is a result of the economic fallacy that we cannot afford to control pollution."

Actually, as Udall implies, we can afford it. It has been estimated that the cost of purifying all of the water in the United States would be only about thirty-six dollars per person per year. Once we have caught up with our sewage treatment facility building and our research, the cost would be lower.

Right now it costs us more to suffer the hardships of water pollution than it would to clean up the mess. James

J. Flannery, Chief Economist of the Federal Water Pollution Control Administration, estimates that the price we pay for the effects of water pollution may run as high as seven billion dollars per year. This includes losses in crops, cattle, and other possessions. But no price tag can be placed on the loss of health because of water-borne disease, or the loss of pleasure because of water unfit for boating or swimming, or the loss of appetite because of vile-smelling drinking water.

We must act. The situation is rapidly getting out of hand. As of now, we are polluting the waters with too much sewage. By 1980 our sewage wastes in the water will have increased enough to consume, in dry weather, all of the oxygen in the twenty-two principal river systems of the United States. Our rubbish production rose from less than three pounds per day per person in 1920 to almost five pounds per day per person in 1967. In San Francisco, the rate is an astonishing eight pounds daily per resident.

John W. Gardner, the former Secretary of Health, Education, and Welfare, has summed up the whole problem beautifully. "The time has come," he said, "for man to make the environment his ally and not his enemy."

17

How Goes the War?

Chanute, Kansas, had water during the summer of 1952. Of course, the Neosho River, where the drinking water came from, was low. But then it was low every summer. What the people of this small town did not know was that they were not going to get any more rain for almost five years.

After a few months, Chanute's citizens were using all kinds of measures to conserve water. Then they decided to build a dam across the river. By the fall of 1956, the dam was all ready—and then the river went dry. The only remedy for the water shortage was to build a dirt dam and trap all of the town's sewage water. For five months, the sewage water was reclaimed and sent back through the faucets of Chanute's homes. It was yellow, ugly looking water, and it had foam in it. Then, at last, the rains came.

It took this horrible experience to make the people decide that clear water was worth the expense. They built three new dams, and now the town has an ample supply of water. Perhaps Chanute was lucky. Perhaps

Principal Areas of Water Pollution in the United States

No locality in the United States is safe from the scourge of water pollution

the drought was necessary to point out the value of fresh water. But how can the people of the rest of the country come to this realization without being forced into an experience such as this?

The federal government may be the only key to the problem. Pollution from Wisconsin may cause trouble in Illinois; pollution in Illinois may cause trouble in Indiana; pollution from Indiana may cause trouble in Kentucky, and so on. It may well be that federal—even international—control is necessary to check water pollution.

But the federal government has always been hampered by weak water pollution-control laws. Until 1948, if a non-navigable river were polluted, the control of the pollution rested with the local authorities. And the local authorities of one state had enough to think about without concerning themselves over the pollution problems in another state, even if theirs was the one that had been doing the polluting.

It wasn't until 1948 that the first Water Control Law was passed in the United States. Under this law, however, the various states retained the primary responsibility for water pollution. The federal government's role was to supply money and certain types of research assistance to the states for the control of water pollution. And if pollution crossed state lines, the government could call a conference to settle the problem. The weak feature of this part of the law was that the offender had as long as six months to clean up the mess. If it didn't, then the federal government would sue the offending state. This process could take years.

In 1965 the law was amended to provide that certain standards of quality were to be set by the federal government. Each state was given until the middle of 1967 to set its own standards, which had to have federal approval or they would have to be changed. The guidelines in this law were general. The standards had to provide for the protection of the public health and the improvement of water quality—nothing more.

If the standards are violated, they must be corrected in three months, or a public hearing will be held and the state will be ordered to correct the situation. However, no penalty can be assessed against the offending state. This is, of course, a weakness in the law.

Since 1965 the law has been broadened. More money has been given to cities, to research installations, and to states to study ways of cleaning up the water. Funds have been allocated to aid in the construction of improved sewage treatment plants. Money is being appropriated to help cities construct separate sewer systems for storm water and sewage water.

The predictions are that the federal government will take more and more notice of water pollution just as it has become more involved in solving air pollution problems. There seems to be a trend away from the feeling that the pollution of air or water is the primary responsibility of the state in which it occurs.

The Clean Waters Restoration Act of 1966 called for the expenditure of almost four billion dollars to construct sewage treatment plants and carry on pollution research, and this already is being considered only a stopgap measure. The plants being built are still able to treat only about 90 percent of the sewage that flows through them, and at that rate they certainly won't be able to keep up with the rise in our population.

The federal government has also set up six regional water pollution-control research laboratories: in Ada, Oklahoma; Athens, Georgia; College, Alaska; Corvallis, Oregon; Cincinnati, Ohio; and Duluth, Minnesota. Several others will be built in the next few years. At these centers, water is studied and research is carried out.

When the problem of water pollution is oil at sea, international cooperation is necessary, since there are international rules about ocean pollution. For example, the most common normal source of oil pollution in the ocean comes from the ballast tanks of ships. As the ship cruises along, it naturally uses up its fuel oil. If no water were taken into the ballast tanks to make up for this loss of weight, the ship would not be stable. Therefore, seawater is pumped aboard. But when the ship takes on more fuel oil, the ballast water is pumped back into the ocean, taking with it some sludge. This is pollution, and international rules have been formulated to prevent the discharge of oily ballast within fifty miles of a coastline.

The Intergovernmental Maritime Consultative Organization, with members from forty nations, has expanded the rule to prohibit the dumping of oily ballast anywhere in the Baltic Sea or the North Sea.

Robert A. Taft Sanitary Engineering Center at Cincinnati, one of the federal government's most up-to-date research centers

We can't rely on our international, federal, state, and local governments to stop all water pollution, however. This job requires the efforts of every citizen. The home-owner who discovers detergent foam in his water; the farmer who finds his cattle dying; the schoolboy who finds garbage in his swimming hole—all must help fight water pollution.

The Federal Water Pollution Control Administration urges every citizen to learn more about water pollution in his own community. Reform can come only through an informed populace. The following questions have been formulated by this agency. The individual who knows the answers has taken the first step toward becoming a valuable fighter in the war against water pollution.

Are wastes treated? Does your community have a sewage treatment plant? What kind of treatment is provided—primary or secondary?

Do wastes escape? In normal dry weather is some sewage bypassed into the stream? In wet weather, when pipes and plants may be taxed by storm-flow, is some sewage bypassed? What percentage? How often does this occur?

Is there an adequate staff? Does your waste treatment plant have enough employees to operate efficiently on a 24-hour, 365-day basis?

Do they have proper training? Does your state provide training programs for plant operators? Does your plant (if it is large enough) provide in-plant training?

If so, are the programs utilized? Does your community pick up the tab for such training courses?

Is the staff certified? Does your state or other agency have certification requirements for plant operators? Does your community live up to these requirements?

Do you have adequate plants and sewers? How many homes are not connected with sewer pipes? How many sewer pipes are not connected with a waste treatment plant? Is the plant itself modern and up to date? Does your community prohibit connection with roof and other storm water drains?

What are your future needs? Has your community drafted a plan to build new sewers and new plants as its area grows?

If you can answer these questions, you know what steps must be taken in your community to prevent or control water pollution. Then, as was suggested in the case of air pollution, you can help make your fellow students, your parents, and even your community aware of the problem. We are being attacked on all sides by water pollution of all types from all kinds of sources. Only by first being informed and then by taking action can we prevent ourselves from being strangled in our own garbage.

18

Our Noisy World

We live in a noisy world. The roar of jets, the screech of tires, the hum of fans and air-conditioners, the blaring of radio and television, all pound in our ears twenty-four hours every day.

Even in one of the most isolated sections of the United States, the noise pollution from jet aircraft has caused a great deal of damage. In northeastern Arizona, the relics of the cave dwellings at the Canyon de Chelly National Monument have been partially destroyed. Sonic booms from jets have caused about eighty tons of rock to fall. Some of the rock spires in Utah's Bryce Canyon have been shaken by this type of noise, too. Fifteen tons of dirt and rock have been dislodged there.

Make no mistake, noise is as much a contaminant of our environment as smoke or detergent foam.

There are quiet places on earth, but we have to travel far to reach them. A tribe of Africans, called the Maban, live in a quiet zone of the southeastern Sudan. The background noise in their communities is measured at about one-tenth of the sound made by a running electric refrigerator. They have no manufacturing plants or automobiles—no cattle or other animals except chickens. What little noise they do have is muffled by the vegetation, since there is no concrete highway or other sound-reflecting surface nearby.

Dr. Samuel Rosen, a research physician, has made three trips to study these people, and he has discovered some amazing things about the effects of noise on a human. He found, for example, that more than half of the Mabans who are from seventy to seventy-nine years of age can hear sounds only 2 percent of the people in our culture in that age range can hear. And not only that, but the average Maban in his seventies can hear as well as the average New Yorker in his twenties. Dr. Rosen concluded that noise pollution is a serious cause of hearing loss.

The noise that surrounds us can be merely an annoyance, but it can also produce physical pain and even destroy parts of our bodies or drive us insane. But what is it?

The layman might define noise as unwanted sound, which, of course, is not an accurate definition, because what is unwanted sound to some people may be desirable sound to others. We all have heard stories about city people being unable to sleep during their vacations in the country because they missed the noise.

Sound—and therefore noise—is measured in decibels. A decibel is an abstract unit, so a few examples are necessary if it is to be understood. Ordinary speech has a loudness of about sixty decibels, and the normal human can hear sounds over a range of one hundred and

Jet aircraft are not only noise polluters, but air polluters as well

thirty decibels. Mice have been killed by sounds that measure one hundred and seventy-five decibels.

A subway train, a diesel truck, or a gunshot can produce about one hundred decibels. A power mower or a discotheque may hit one hundred and seven decibels, and an incoming jet one hundred and seventeen. The normal background noise in a quiet suburban neighborhood ranges from twenty to thirty decibels, while the average Manhattan hotel room's background noise is from fifty to sixty; and on the streets of Manhattan, the noise may reach one hundred and three decibels.

But it is not only the intensity of the sound that makes it unpleasant. A low note on an organ is not as ear-shattering as a high note, even if they are both played at the same degree of intensity, as measured in decibels.

A sound wave may also be measured by the number of times per second the wave hits our ear—in other words, by the frequency of the wave. It is measured in cycles per second. The note "A" above "middle C" on a piano has a frequency of four hundred and forty cycles per second. The more frequent the cycles per second, the higher the note. Our ears are most sensitive to sounds of about two thousand cycles per second. The lowest note that most people can hear is about eighteen cycles per second; the highest is about eighteen thousand cycles per second.

Thus sound is a hard thing to measure, since its loudness is a combination of two things: frequency and intensity. How it affects us is a matter of how many times per second the waves hit the ear and how much energy the waves have at that instant. There is even a third factor: how long a time does the noise continue? But since we are talking about noise pollution, we will have to assume that the noise persists long enough to be annoying. Few people mind the sound of a courthouse clock striking every hour. Indeed, it may be soothing. But let that same clock start striking every second, and it becomes noise.

The real noise pollutants are not minor noises. When a driver of a car starts the engine and tries to talk at the same time, he may not be heard. But the car is soon started, and the noise turns out to be merely a passing thing, not a pollutant.

The real noise pollutants can destroy not only rocks and monuments, but also the bodies and minds of men. In a recent survey of men in the United States, it was found that there are about five million males between the ages of ten and fifty-nine with hearing losses. One million of these need hearing aids. The situation is even more serious for those who are from seventy to seventy-nine years old: 56 percent of them need hearing aids, even if they do not wear them.

Noise does affect our hearing. When tests were made on people who worked in a bottling plant, it was found that those who had worked there for four years were beginning to suffer hearing losses. Workers with "tender" ears, naturally, were the first to experience difficulty in hearing. But in the group of people who had worked in the plant for ten years, even the "average" ears and the "tough" ears had entered the hearing-loss department.

This study points up the fact that exposure to continual noise will damage almost anyone's hearing, although some of us are more susceptible than others. The usual pattern is that workers in noisy factories, for example, develop a ringing in their ears which goes away when they leave their jobs at night. But a day may come when the ringing does not stop, and then they are on the road to permanent deafness.

Constant noise may cause our blood vessels to contract, our skin to become pale, our muscles to constrict, and adrenaline to be shot into our bloodstreams. This adrenaline produces tension and nervousness. Even office workers can suffer from noise pollution. They are surrounded by clicking typewriters, ringing phones, clattering office machines, and other people's conversations. This noise may produce temper tantrums, headaches, fatigue, and even nausea.

At the Mie Prefectural University School of Medicine, in Japan, it was found that the ammonia levels in the brain, liver, and blood of rats increased when the rats were subjected to one hundred decibels of noise for a few days. Of course, some rats were affected in a few hours, and some were not affected at all. The cause was not an increased ammonia production rate. It was a breakdown in the body's ability to get rid of this chemical. Rats at the University of South Dakota developed heart enlargements and increased cholesterol levels when they lived in noisy surroundings.

At the Max Planck Institute in West Germany it has been found that ironworkers not only have physical problems caused by noise, but mental problems as well. There is a higher proportion of family difficulties among these men than there is among the same number of people working in quieter surroundings.

No one knows what the effects of noise on the mind really are. What is disturbing to one person may not be disturbing to another. Every parent of a teen-ager becomes aware of this as he watches his son or daughter finish a homework assignment with a radio blaring away. When people first begin to work in a noisy place, they are inefficient, but they soon get used to the noise. Then, if the noise is turned off, the workers become inefficient again until they get used to the quiet.

The type of noise most disturbing to our subconscious is not the continual noise, but the sudden, loud, surprising noise. Intermittent noise can be very disturbing if you live near a jet airport or across the street from a building construction site. It is the on-again, off-again type of noise pollution that leads to nervousness.

Dr. Aram Glorig, the director of Dallas' Callier Hearing and Speech Center, classifies noise pollution according to its mental effects. The first of these is speech interference. In this category are the noises that, although they may not damage hearing, are annoying and interfere with normal speech communication. Even an air-conditioner can create this kind of pollution.

In the second group are noises that cause inefficiency in carrying out motor or mental tasks. This type of pollution is most often found where the noise level keeps changing—in offices near railroad tracks, for example.

The third group of noises are those that bring about physiological changes. These occur when the noise pollution is not only loud, but unexpected. The noise may come, for example, from blasting operations or from an airport. The sudden noise may startle anyone nearby and cause muscle contraction. It may also bring on a rise in blood pressure, an increase in breathing rate or heartbeat, and the production of excess sweat.

Finally, there is the effect brought about by annoyance. There is no way of defining this, since sounds that may annoy one person may have no effect on another. But as anyone knows who has listened to a barking dog all night, noises that cause a prolonged period of annoyance can have a tremendous effect on the mind.

19

Toward a Quieter World

A great deal of scientific investigation has been carried out in connection with one of our chief noise polluters—the jet airplane. Constant monitoring of takeoff noises goes on at some of our larger airports. And the pilot who causes his plane to offend the ears more than necessary is reprimanded.

Still we have a long way to go in order to bring the noise of aircraft down to an acceptable level. An additional problem is the sonic boom caused by some of our supersonic airplanes, which are major polluters. A few years ago, the federal government tried to find out how irritating these booms were to the people on the ground.

In Oklahoma City, Oklahoma, a town that had been suffering from an average of about two hundred booms per month, the citizens were asked for their reactions to all of the noise. After living with the booms for six months, 25 percent of the people in the city said that they had not learned to cope with the problem. The sonic booms were still startling them, interrupting their sleep, and, in general, making their lives unbearable.

A special acoustical room at the NASA/Marshall Space Flight Center in Huntsville, Alabama. Even the noise of big space-launch vehicles must be measured, and this is the room where they calibrate the monitoring instruments

The problem of aircraft noise pollution has become a serious one even in Norway. The Norwegian Aircraft Noise Commission, working with the Institute of Physics of the University of Oslo, has been monitoring noise in the Oslo area. Airplanes have been channeled along paths where they will make the fewest number of people unhappy, and their takeoff procedures are observed. Microphones on poles all over the city give the scientists the information they need, then "noise maps" are made to determine the best pathways and climb patterns for the airplanes to use.

But we still don't know when a noise is really annoying. Dr. W. Hawel of the Max Planck Institute has developed what he calls an "annoyance level meter." He takes the personality of the hearer (good or bad temper) into account. He also measures the physical situation of the place where the noise is heard, the activity of the listener, the quality of the sound, and the intensity of the sound. These five readings, although all of them cannot be measured accurately, are fed into a computer. The result is a reading on a scale that ranges from "very annoying" to "very agreeable." If this meter is ever perfected, it could be a great aid to the technician whose task is the elimination of noise pollution.

The need for accurate noise measurement was illustrated in another study. What would you expect to be the noisiest time of day on a big city expressway? The rush hour? Wrong. Dr. Jerome K. Brasch of the University of Michigan found that it is in the middle of the morning, at least on route I-94, on the outskirts of Detroit. The reason: that is the time of peak truck activity.

Another breakthrough was scored by Dr. Edward R. Hermann of Northwestern University, in his study of deafness caused by industrial noise. The real problem here is that the person is seldom aware he is becoming hard of hearing because the change is too gradual. Dr. Hermann came up with a statistical method for predicting oncoming deafness. He developed a way of determining the amount of hearing loss that can be expected in a given industrial environment. With this information he can forecast the rate at which hearing loss will continue if the worker remains at his noisy job.

But while many scientists are trying to find out more and more about noise, its effects, and how to lessen the problem, others are finding out how to make more noise. Canadian engineers have developed a noisemaker that can kill unprotected hearers. It has a tone twice as loud as a Wagnerian soprano at her loudest and sounds like a jet engine. The machine was built originally for a different use: to test the strength of airplane parts at the National Aeronautical Establishment in Ottawa.

The search for a quieter world really started in 1948. That was the year in which an industrial worker won the first lawsuit based upon occupational deafness. And then it seemed that the dam had broken. In the next dozen years there were five hundred noise compensation claims made in the state of California alone. In Florida, Jacksonville's school board sued the local airports because they had made schools unusable on account of noise—and won the case.

Legal action after the damage has been done is not the answer to the problem of noise pollution. Part of the answer may be the use of legal action—before the trouble starts. New York City has laws limiting the playing of radios and television sets, record players and musical instruments, from 11:00 P.M. until 7:00 A.M. Other cities, such as Memphis and Paris, have forbidden automobile drivers to blow their horns. Some British cities prohibit the use of motorcycles during the hours when people are usually sleeping.

But these laws often are broken. And forcing a person to pay a fine is not much consolation to the person whose sleep has been interrupted. A better way of keeping down the noise is to use some sort of damper, such as the muffler on an automobile. This device dissipates some of the noise energy before it is allowed to escape, thus producing weaker sounds. However, the usual type of muffler may tend to cut down on the available power of the engine.

Machines—even the common office typewriter—are often set upon pads or carpets made of rubber or felt to prevent the table, desk, or floor from vibrating along with the machine, thus amplifying the sound.

Acoustical tile is commonly used on the ceilings and walls of noisy rooms. The porous tiles absorb rather than reflect the sound, thus seeming to soak up the sounds that hit them. Sometimes the noises around us must be drowned out. For example, piped-in music in restaurants can cover up the noise of conversation from other tables and the clinking of plates and silverware. An unpleasant noise is thus drowned out by a more pleasant one.

However, we don't seem to be able to reduce very effectively the most annoying noises we have; consequently, we had better protect ourselves from them.

At a conference, Councilman Robert A. Low of New York City suggested better mufflers for construction equipment, trucks, motorcycles, and garbage removal vehicles. He wants less noisy police car sirens, quieter airplanes and helicopters, and better standards for interior and exterior building walls. Mr. Low said: "In so-called modern apartments a shouted question from your wife in one room is likely to be answered by a neighbor through the paper-thin walls of the adjoining apartment."

Councilman Low's requirements are not unreasonable. Dr. Vern O. Knudsen, a physicist who specialized in noise research for many years at the University of California, Los Angeles (he has worn earplugs in bed since 1938), points out that to deaden noises in a building, for instance, would add only 5 or 10 percent to the cost of construction. For that extra cost, says Dr. Knudsen, we can get the equivalent of ten inches of concrete shielding against noise.

The additional cost buys thick, tight, solid-panel entrance doors, insulated walls and ceilings, heavy walls between bathrooms, and double windows. These reduce the noise level by fifty decibels. Laws requiring these construction features are common in Europe. Dr. Knudsen suggests that the United States imitate Sweden, where traffic policemen often carry sound meters in order to bring noise violators to justice.

In the meantime, back at the airport, work continues. Increased interest has been shown in the vertical takeoff and landing (VTOL) and the short takeoff aircraft. Thought has been given to restricting noisy airplanes to special airports. Extra runways might be built to shift air traffic away from heavily populated areas. And the fight still goes on to produce quieter aircraft, although there may not be much hope here, since the fight is also going on to produce bigger supersonic airplanes with more powerful engines.

Many people think that the electric car may be a boon to noise pollution as well as air pollution control. This type of vehicle is practically noiseless.

And on one other front, Dr. Burton King, director of the hearing clinic of Duke University's Medical Center, had a suggestion. Go-Go Girls in discotheques, he said, should wear earmuffs. Otherwise they may become deaf from all the noise.

20

People, People, People

One of our biggest problems seems to be that there are too many of us. And there are more of us each day than there were the day before. More of us are buying automobiles, more of us are making noise, more of us are dumping sewage into open waters, more of us are burning trash, and more of us are using foaming detergents.

The creators of pollution, whether it be air pollution, water pollution, or noise pollution, are human beings. And the more human beings there are, the more pollution, and the harder we have to work to control it. If we work as hard as we can, perhaps we can keep ahead of the population explosion.

As things stand now, every time your heart beats, the world's population increases by one person—almost two hundred and seventy-five thousand babies are born into the world every day. But only about one hundred and fifty-five thousand people die each day. That's a net gain of about one hundred and twenty thousand people in the world every twenty-four hours.

The daily increase in the birthrate will not remain

There are a lot of people in the world, and they all seem to be going somewhere in vehicles that pollute

constant for very long. As these babies grow up, the larger adult population will add still larger numbers to the population. People, people, people. Pollution, pollution, and more pollution.

In 1967, we had about three and one-half billion people in the world. Over half of them live in Asia. Sixteen percent of them live in Africa and Latin America. The rest can be found on the continents of North America and Europe, in the polar regions, on oceanic islands, and in western Russia.

By 1980 we should have well over four billion people in the world. Latin America alone is expected to increase its population by almost 60 percent. Where are we going to put all these people, and what are we going to do about the pollution they create? Some population experts predict that in six hundred years every square foot of land surface on the face of the earth could be covered by people. We may have to put them in two-thousand-story apartment buildings. But, as yet, we don't know how to build them that high.

What a pollution problem! We are doubling the world's population every thirty-seven years.

In all the centuries that man has been upon the earth—until our own twentieth century—the world's population increased less than one percent per year. At the beginning of the Christian era there were only about two and one-half million people in the world. The mark of one billion was not reached until about 1880. Today, we are increasing at the rate of about 2 percent per year.

If this enormous growth rate keeps up, it is possible that the number of people on earth will hit seven billion by the year 2000.

Always before, something came along to offset the birthrate. Sometimes huge numbers of people starved to death. But now our agricultural science is so advanced and our methods of transportation are so streamlined that, in most parts of the world, people don't starve.

Epidemics of disease used to eliminate large populations. At the present time, large-scale epidemics usually occur only in those backward parts of the world where modern medicine is unknown.

Man also has conquered the wild animals that used to attack him, and he has learned to live in places where he could not live before, such as the desert and the polar regions. Almost the only limiting factor, besides war, facing man today is his own pollution. What can we do about it?

Some people recommend that we send vast numbers of our people into outer space to find homes on other planets. This probably wouldn't work, since experts predict that if we could live on Venus, for example, its population would match the earth's in about thirty-seven years. Then, too, there is the problem of finding enough spaceships to do the job. Even if we knew how to send people off the earth and keep them alive, where would we get the hardware? Just to keep the population level of the earth at a constant number, by the year 2030 we would have to launch one thousand spaceships per day, with each ship carrying one thousand people.

It seems apparent that we must turn to science and technology to help us conquer the noise in our air, the ever-present filth which darkens our skies, and the garbage which is contaminating our clear water. With so many people in the world—and more to come—we cannot close our eyes and hope that our problems will go away.

21

Your Future
in Pollution Control

What of the future? Morris Nieburger, a meteorologist at the University of California, Los Angeles, tells us that the air from across the Pacific Ocean is clean when it reaches the West Coast of the United States. It picks up pollution in the western states, drops some of it when it passes over the Rocky Mountains, and then collects more and more as it travels over the country on its way toward the eastern seaboard.

But, he points out, what if the eight hundred million people in China owned automobiles in the same proportion as the people in Los Angeles do—almost one for every adult. The air coming in would be polluted before it reached our shores. Gradually the world would be covered with smog and particle fallout. Mankind would perish—strangled by its own aerial garbage. Equally frightening pictures could be called to mind concerning water and noise pollution.

What is the answer? How can we solve this worldwide problem? At best, in some places we are holding our own. At worst, in some places the land is becoming denuded and people are dying. The final solutions, if they are found at all and in time, must be found by the coming generations.

There is a shortage of competent scientific and engineering man power in the field of pollution control. For years, workers in the field of sanitary and environmental science have been laboring in an unglamorous, unrecognized, and unrewarded field. They have not enjoyed the prestige of the aeronautical engineer, the electronic researcher, or the medical scientist.

In a recent National Science Foundation list of technical personnel, it was stated that there were, in the United States, fewer than five thousand sanitary engineers. Worse than that, only one hundred were in training in this field. The public is now ready to listen to the scientists and technicians. But where are the scientists and technicians who are skilled in solving the pollution problems?

Some stopgap measures have been suggested. Retraining is one. The smoke inspector, for example, can be taught some chemistry. Scientists can be recruited from other fields, such as the aerospace industry. Chemical engineers can be transferred to pollution-control agencies.

But to attract truly competent people, the pollution-control field must be made more rewarding. Money is now being funneled into loans, scholarships, and research programs to aid in the preparation of pollution experts. The federal government is offering graduate training grants, research fellowships, research grants, and technical training grants to qualified students. It is also encouraging states to offer training programs for pollution personnel, as well as short-course programs to upgrade people who are at present working in the field. The field is being made as attractive to students as possible. Let us hope that we are not too late and that our youth will become interested in preparing for a career in this vital work.

To begin with, we desperately need meteorologists who will study the pollution problem. The weather is the medium of transportation for the substances that pollute our air. The speed, direction, and height of winds determine what will be transported and how far it will travel. But as yet we cannot predict winds with any great degree of accuracy, nor can we be completely sure when and where it will rain or snow and drop pollutants to earth.

Furthermore, we do not completely understand the cause of air inversions—those air conditions that hold the smog over our cities. Great breakthroughs have occurred in the processing of weather data. We have learned to use computers, and we have developed nationwide and even worldwide systems of data recording. But the sad truth is that we still do not really know enough about what causes weather or how to predict it.

We need organic chemists, inorganic chemists, and analytical chemists who can study the pollution brought about by our many new industrial processes. Every time a new production technique is tried in a factory, there is a chance that a new source of pollution may be born.

A chemist might use a gas chromatograph to analyze the pollution content in water samples

Chemists are needed to work on devices to trap this pollution, whether it be solid, gaseous, or noisy. They are also needed to help remove pollution from the air and water once it is there.

The hydrologist, the soil scientist, the limnologist, the oceanographer, and the biological and medical researchers are valuable pollution fighters, too. Various plants absorb polluted gases and polluted water in various ways, and we need to know how this is done. Perhaps the outcome of such research may be the discovery or creation of types of plants that are immune to various kinds of air and water pollution. We also must know more about the connections between air and water pollution and the diseases of animals and men.

Physicists, too, can help in the fight. The whole problem of the transfer and diffusion of gases and water

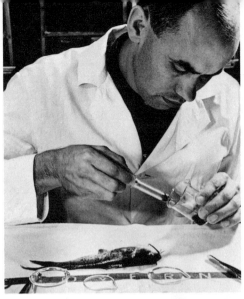

A biologist might study a dead fish to find out the effects of a pollutant. Dr. Donald Mount of the U.S. Public Health Service prepares for the autopsy

He then takes a blood sample

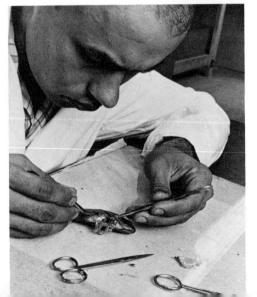

Then comes the real work

from one location to another, especially over a large area, must be studied. In addition, more effective ways of filtering air, water, and noise can be developed by physicists. They need to discover more about the electrostatic properties of pollutants so that better methods of trapping can be developed.

Sanitary and civil engineers, of course, will be in the front lines of the war against pollution, designing municipal incinerators, sewage treatment plants, and noise reduction devices. But other types of engineers are essential to the task. We need electrical, mechanical, and agricultural engineers to accomplish our purposes.

Scientists and engineers are not the only ones who can join in the crusade. The city planners are necessary, too. Better zoning laws are required. As cities expand, a great deal of thought must be given to the passage of adequate antipollution legislation.

Many new businesses have recently been set up to combat pollution. These are the pollution-control companies, and they desperately need skilled personnel. Business is booming in the filtration industry and the water purifying industry, and the end of the boom is not yet in sight.

Most of these occupations, of course, require college training. Some of them call for graduate degrees, such as the M.S. or M.A., or even the Ph.D. or M.D.; but there are pollution fighters who lack college diplomas. With a little education beyond high school, technicians can join in the research. They can measure and record air, water, and noise pollution indexes. They can compile weather records. They can assist in the experimentation carried on in both scientific and engineering laboratories.

There are many occupational opportunities for young people with only high-school diplomas. There are always openings for persons interested in the raising of and caring for living plants and animals in the experimental laboratories and for those who want to work in pollution-disposal installations. There also are countless office jobs—receptionists, file clerks, telephone operators —which can be filled by people who want to assist the scientists, engineers, and technicians in their war against pollution.

There are other jobs in the pollution-control field which do not require more than a high-school diploma.

Laboratory assistants may record data in air pollution experiments

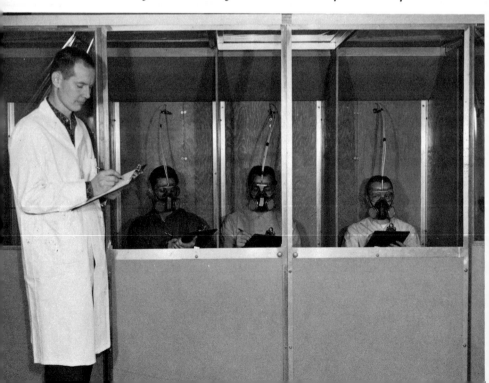

They are for those people who are responsible for the day-to-day operation of the pollution-control plants and may be concerned with the maintenance of the sewage treatment plant or the recording apparatus in the air pollution laboratory.

Suppose that you want to work in a pollution-control laboratory or industry. There are three types of positions open to you. You can become a scientist or an engineer; you can become a technician; or you can become a clerical worker.

The best way to start preparing to become a scientist or an engineer in the pollution field is to specialize in mathematics and science in high school. You should take physics, chemistry, and biology—as many courses as possible—and you should have studied algebra, plane and solid geometry, and trigonometry before you graduate.

But you cannot ignore the fields of English, history, and language either, since the development of the art of communication is essential to the job of being a scientist or an engineer. Reports must be written, speeches must be made, and perhaps even magazine articles must be created.

Scientists must have at least a master's degree, if not a doctorate, and engineers need at least a bachelor's degree. The required courses include a heavy concentration of science and mathematics as well as social studies and the humanities.

Closely allied to the scientists and the engineers in the field of pollution control are the technicians. It is estimated that four technicians are needed for every scientist

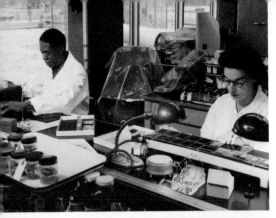

Technicians may study the tissues of animals killed by air pollution

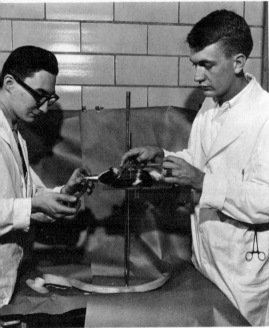

They may expose live animals to air pollution in scientific experiments

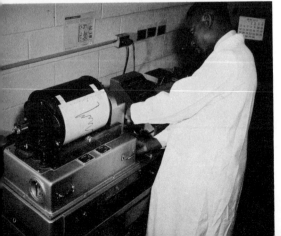

And they may use complicated machines such as this spectrometer to study light penetration

or engineer who is working in a laboratory. Usually, a technician needs a junior college or community college diploma, but more and more common is the technician with a bachelor of science degree.

Technicians can perform routine duties such as cleaning glassware and feeding animals. They may also have more complicated standard duties, such as recording the data from experiments. If they are well educated and highly skilled, they may even be responsible for some special duties, such as carrying on their own experiments with a minimum of supervision.

Clerical workers, whether they are secretaries, typists, telephone operators, shipping and receiving clerks, or bookkeepers, usually take a clerical curriculum in high school. Many of them also have diplomas from business colleges. One type of highly skilled clerical worker—the computer programmer—needs to know a great deal about mathematics. These workers generally have a college degree, although there are some junior and community colleges that now offer courses in programming.

Here are some sources for more information on careers in the pollution-control field:

Biologist, health
 National Institutes of Health
 Bethesda, Maryland 20014

Biologist, research
 American Institute of Biological Sciences
 3900 Wisconsin Avenue, N.W.
 Washington, D.C. 20016

Chemist
   American Chemical Society
   1155 16th Street, N.W.
   Washington, D.C.   20036

Clerical Worker
   United Business Schools Association
   1518 K Street, N.W.
   Washington, D.C.   20005

Engineer, Agricultural
   American Society of Agricultural Engineers
   420 Main Street
   St. Joseph, Michigan   49085

Engineer, Chemical
   American Institute of Chemical Engineers
   345 East 47th Street
   New York, New York   10017

Engineer, Civil
   American Society of Civil Engineers
   345 East 47th Street
   New York, New York   10017

Engineer, Industrial
   American Institute of Industrial Engineers
   345 East 47th Street
   New York, New York   10017

Engineer, Mechanical
   American Society of Mechanical Engineers
   345 East 47th Street
   New York, New York   10017

Engineer, Metallurgical and Mining
   American Institute of Mining, Metallurgical, and
      Petroleum Engineers
   345 East 47th Street
   New York, New York   10017

Fish and Wildlife Specialist
    Fish and Wildlife Service
    United States Department of the Interior
    Washington, D.C.   20240

Forester
    United States Forest Service
    United States Department of Agriculture
    Washington, D.C.   20250

Geographer
    Association of American Geographers
    1146 16th Street, N.W.
    Washington, D.C.   20036

Geologist
    American Geological Institute
    1444 N Street, N.W.
    Washington, D.C.   20005

Hydrologist
    American Geophysical Union
    1145 19th Street, N.W.
    Washington, D.C.   20036

Meteorologist
    American Meteorological Society
    45 Beacon Street
    Boston, Massachusetts   02108

Oceanographer
    American Society of Limnology and Oceanography
    Department of Oceanography
    Oregon State University
    Corvallis, Oregon   97331

Pharmacist
    American Pharmaceutical Association
    2215 Constitution Avenue N.W.
    Washington, D.C.   20037

Physician, Public Health
    American Medical Association
    535 North Dearborn Street
    Chicago, Illinois   60610

Physicist
    American Institute of Physics
    335 East 45th Street
    New York, New York   10017

Programmer, Computer
    American Federation of Information Processing Societies
    Post Office Box 1196
    Santa Monica, California   90406

Psychologist
    American Psychological Association
    1200 17th Street, N.W.
    Washington, D.C.   20036

Soil Scientist
    Soil Conservation Society of America
    7515 Ankeny Road
    Ankeny, Iowa   50021

Technician, Engineering and Scientific
    American Society of Certified Engineering Technicians
    2029 K Street, N.W.
    Washington, D.C.   20006

Urban Planner
    American Institute of Planners
    917 15th Street, N.W.
    Washington, D.C.   20005

The nation—even the world—needs more young people who want to work in the pollution-control field. As Hubert H. Humphrey said to the winners of the Science Talent Search: "Technology-rooted problems—air, water, and noise pollution—cannot be solved by giving up technology. No, the solution is not to stop thinking. It is to think even harder and more comprehensively. It is the opportunity of your generation to insure that the world may never be subjected to the ultimate harm and destruction that lie within man's capacity."

Bibliography

Aylesworth, Thomas G., *Our Polluted World*. American Education Publications, Inc., Columbus, Ohio, 1966.

Battan, Louis J., *The Unclean Sky*. Doubleday and Company, Inc., Garden City, New York, 1966.

Carr, Donald E., *Death of the Sweet Waters*. W. W. Norton and Company, Inc., New York, N.Y., 1966.

Cousins, Norman, et al, *Freedom to Breathe*. Business Council for Clean Air, New York, N.Y., 1966.

Edelson, Edward, *The Battle for Clean Air*. Public Affairs Pamphlets, New York, N.Y., 1967.

Edelson, Edward, and Warshofsky, Fred, *Poisons in the Air*. Pocket Books, Inc., New York, N.Y., 1966.

Edinger, James G., *Watching for the Wind*. Doubleday and Company, Inc., Garden City, New York, 1967.

Halacy, D. S., Jr., *The Water Crisis*. E. P. Dutton and Company, Inc., New York, N.Y., 1966.

Herber, Lewis, *Crisis in Our Cities*. Prentice-Hall, Inc., Englewood Cliffs, New Jersey, 1965.

Kavaler, Lucy, *Dangerous Air*. The John Day Company, New York, N.Y., 1967.

Mellanby, Kenneth, *Pesticides and Pollution*. Collins, London, England, 1967.

Munzer, Martha E., *Planning Our Town*. Alfred A. Knopf, New York, N.Y., 1964.

Perry, John, *Our Polluted World: Can Man Survive?* Franklin Watts, Inc., New York, N.Y., 1967.

Wise, William, *Killer Smog*. Rand McNally & Company, Chicago, Illinois, 1968.

Index

Printed in U.S.A.